Big Little Books:
The Whitman Publishing Company's Golden Age, 1932-1938

An Exhibition from the
Duane H. Siers Family Collection

June 21-September 20, 2002

By James A. Findlay

BIENES CENTER FOR THE LITERARY ARTS
The Dianne & Michael Bienes Special Collections and Rare Book Library
Broward County Libraries Division
Fort Lauderdale, Florida
2002

ISBN: 096788585X
First edition

Bienes Center for the Literary Arts
Broward County Main Library, 6th Floor
100 S. Andrews Avenue
Ft. Lauderdale, FL 33301

www.broward.org/bienes

Table of Contents

#1

#129

Introduction

The selection of 136 **Big Little Books** (BLBs) on exhibition in the galleries of the Bienes Center for the Literary Arts is part of a larger collection of approximately 425 titles[1] donated to Broward County Libraries Division in 1986 by Mr. Duane H. Siers of Deerfield Beach, Florida. The exhibit features only the 136 titles[2] in the Siers collection that were published by the Whitman Publishing Company (Racine, Wisconsin) during its "Golden Age," 1932-1938.

Big Little Book® was the collective (i.e, series) title given to the volumes Whitman published: the name promised "the buyer a great amount of reading material and pleasure (BIG) within a small and compact (LITTLE) book"[3], i.e., approximately 5" (height) x 3" (width) x 1½" (depth). Children were enthralled by the "comic book" nature of the publications since each book generally had a text page and an accompanying facing illustration. Individual titles were commonly published in editions of hundreds of thousands and were sold inexpensively in stores throughout the nation to an anxiously awaiting audience of young readers.

Represented in the exhibit are some of the best known American and British comic book, radio program, movie title, and children's classics characters from the 1930s and 40s, including Dick Tracy, Buck Rogers, Mickey Mouse, Little Orphan Annie, Louisa M. Alcott's *Little Men*, Robert Louis Stevenson's *Treasure Island*, Flash Gordon, The Lone Ranger, The G-Man, Li'l Abner, Little Miss Muffet, Popeye the Sailor, Tarzan, Donald Duck, Gene Autry, Walt Disney's Snow White and the Seven Dwarfs and Wimpy, the hamburger eater.

---

[1] Deerfield couple donate Big Little Books / by Steven Sands. – [Boca Raton, FL?]: **Jewish Journal**, p. 25B+ (Oct. 23, 1986)

[2] Approximately 269 titles, excluding peripherals, were published between 1932-1938 by Whitman Publishing Company, Racine, Wisconsin. For a complete listing see: **Lowery's The collector's guide to Big Little Books and similar books**, 1981. A second, revised and corrected edition has been announced as forthcoming.

[3] Lower, Larry. **Lowery's The collector's guide to Big Little Books and similar books.** – [Danville, CA]: Educational Research and Applications Corporation, 1981, p. 2.

Mr. Siers began collecting BLBs when he was a child. He was 11 years old in 1945 when his mother gave him his first Big Little Books[4]. That quintessential maternal act led to a lifetime of reading pleasure and of collecting and caring for his cherished BLBs. He said of that period in his life, "I loved those books and spent hours and hours reading . . . My favorite position was to lie on the rug by the sofa, propped up on one arm. When that arm got tired, I'd switch to the other. I didn't know there was any other way to read."[5] He continued to accumulate new volumes even into his adult years. The collection also grew significantly from the addition of gifts he received from family, friends and business colleagues who were aware of his collecting interests.

In the middle 1980s, Mr. Siers considered giving his collection to an orphanage or other charitable institution but thought that perhaps the volumes would not be properly cared for and preserved so in 1986 he opted instead to donate them to the Broward County Libraries Division's Main Library rare book room.

Because BLBs were cheaply produced on highly acidic paper, it is unusual to find copies in mint condition and the Duane H. Siers collection is no exception. The titles were read and handled by the young Mr. Siers with little thought given to their long-term preservation and, consequently, their current condition mirrors the heavy usage they were subjected to: some titles are missing pages, several lack spines and/or covers and many of them are dog-eared and frayed.

However, in fulfilling the wishes of Duane H. Siers to preserve his cherished titles for posterity, the collection is now housed in the humidity, light and temperature controlled state-of-the-art vault of the five-year old Dianne and Michael Bienes Special Collections and Rare Book Library where it will permanently be at the disposal of curious children and adults of all ages.

---

4 The rare essentials [Bienes Center opens] / by Elisa Turner. – Miami, FL: **The Miami Herald**, p 1I + 7 (Jan. 12, 1997)

5 Ibid.

Exhibition Checklist

T he following descriptions are from a selection of actual titles in the Bienes Center's **Duane H. Siers Family Collection of Big Little Books**. All of the titles were published by Whitman Publishing Company, Racine, Wisconsin between 1932-1938.

The exhibition checklist is arranged chronologically by earliest date. Within date, arrangement is alphabetical by title (as it appears on the title page; other titles, i.e., alternate and cover titles are given in the notes). When identified, the following elements are also given: date, artist, author, other personal and/or corporate authors, title, edition statement, place of publication, publisher, copyright holder and date (if different from publisher's copyright), date of publication, actual numbered pages and/or cover to cover pagination, illustration statement, size (height x width x depth), series title, series number and notes.

Brackets [ ] are used to enclose information taken from sources other than the actual books in hand.

Key to abbreviations:
    b & w ills. = black and white illustration(s)
    c = copyright
    cm. = centimeters
    Co. = Company
    col. ills. = color illustration(s)
    i.e. = that is
    ills. = illustrations
    p. or pp. = page(s)
    & = and
    WI - Wisconsin

Classification numbers given in the notes section are from the following reference:
    i.e., Lowery, 1981 =
    Lowery's The collector's guide to big little books and similar books / [by Lawrence F. Lowery]. – Danville, CA: (P.O. Box 732, Danville 94526): Education Research and Applications Corp., 1981. – 378 p.: ill.; 22 x 13.5 x 3 cm.

#2

inside front cover. – Publisher's advertisement. – p. [296]. – "Date [i.e., 1927] is copyright date of the comic strip; BLB was published in 1933." – Lowery, 1981, p. 29. – Library's copy lacking pp. [3-4]. – **Houdini's big little book of magic; easy for everyone; 145 magic tricks by Houdini and other magicians**" – On front cover].

1 1932
Gould, Chester [artist & author]
Dick Tracy, the detective / by Chester Gould. – Whitman Publishing Company, (c1932, Chester Gould), c1932. – 316, i.e., [320] p.: b & w ills.; col. ills. on covers; 11 x 10.5 x 3.5 cm. – (The big little book; W-707)

[Notes: "GW2" – Lowery, 1981. – Hard covers. – **"The adventures of Dick Tracy, detective** by Chester Gould" – On front cover. – "Known to 10,000,000 readers" – On front cover. – "First BLB to be published" – Lowery, 1981, p. 28. – Library's copy lacking spine].

2 1933
Houdini, Harry, 1874-1926 [author]
Houdini, Beatrice, 1876-1943 [author]
Book of magic: fascinating puzzles, tricks and mysterious stunts / selected by Houdini; the world's greatest magician. – Racine, WI: Whitman Publishing Company (c1927 by Beatrice Houdini, Executrix of the Estate of Harry Houdini), c1927 [1933]. – 295, i.e., [300] p.: b & w ills.; col. ills. on cover; 11.5 x 10.5 x 4 cm. – ([The big little book]; no. 715)

[Notes: "GW8" – Lowery, 1981. – Hard covers & soft spine. – "Duane H. Siers" – Stamped on

3 1933
Calkins, Dick [artist]
Nowlan, Phil [author]
Buck Rogers in the Twenty-fifth Century A.D. / by Lt. Dick Calkins and Phil Nowlan. – Racine, WI: Whitman Publishing Company, (c1933, John F. Dille Co., Chicago, Ill.), c1933. – 314, i.e., [320] p.: b & w ills.; col. ills. on covers & spine. – (The big little book; 742)

[Copy 1: Notes: "GW23" – Lowery, 1981. – Hard covers & soft spine. – Publisher's advertisement. – p. [316]. – "**Buck Rogers: 25th Century A.D.**" – On front cover & spine].

[Copy 2: Notes: "GW23" – Lowery, 1981. – Hard covers & soft spine. – Publisher's advertisement. – p. [316]. – "**Buck Rogers: 25th Century A.D.**" – On front cover & spine. – Library's copy 2 lacking pp. [3-4 & spine].

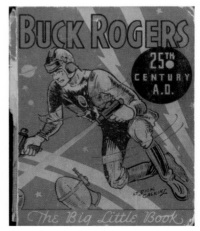

#3

#4

#7

#5

#8

#6

#8.5

4 1933
Arbo, Hal [artist]
Morgan, Leon [author]
Cowboy stories / by Leon Morgan; illustrated by Hal Arbo of the W Lazy 5 Ranch. – Racine, WI: Whitman Publishing Company, c1933. – 294. i.e., [300] p.: b & w ills.; col. ills. on covers & spine; 11.5 x 11 x 3.5 cm. – (The big little book; 724)

[Notes: "GW18" – Lowery, 1981. – Hard covers & soft spine. – "Duane H. Siers" – Stamped on inside front cover. – Publisher's advertisement. – p. [296].

5 1933
Willard, Frank [artist & author]
Kayo and Moon Mullins. – Racine, WI: Whitman Publishing Company (c1933, Frank Willard), c1933. – 310 [incomplete copy] i.e., [320] p.: b & w ills.; col. ills. on covers; 11.5 x 9 x 3.5 cm. – (The big little book; [746])

[Copy 1: Notes: "GW26" – Lowery, 1981. – Hard covers. – Library's copy lacking spine, back cover & pp. [311-320]. – Peach-colored title page. – "**Moon Mullins and Ka Yo**" – On front cover. – "Hope Branum from Miss Katharine Grey" – Signed in pencil on p.[3]. – "Also produced as a givaway – See Peripherals GWp13, p. 102. – Lowery, 1981, p. 34" (SEE #8.5 in this checklist)].

[Copy 2: Notes: "GW26" – Lowery, 1981. – Hard covers. – Library's copy lacking spine & pp. [3-8]. – Publisher's advertisement. – p. [316]. – "**Moon Mullins and Ka Yo**" – On front cover. – "Pushbottom; Emmy; Eillie; Mamie; Egypt" – Pictured on back cover. – "Also produced as a givaway – See Peripherals GWp13, p. 102. – Lowery, 1981, p. 34" (SEE #8.5 in this checklist)].

6 1933
Gray, Harold, 1894-1968
[artist & author]
Little Orphan Annie and Sandy / by Harold Gray. – Racine, WI: Whitman Publishing Company (c1933, Harold Gray), c1933. – 316, i.e., [320] p.: b & w ills.; col. ills. on covers; 11 x 10 x 3.5 cm. – (The big little book; 716)

[Notes: "GW9" – Lowery, 1981. – Hard covers & soft spine. – Publisher's advertisement – p. [318] – "Virginia Branum, Camp Nawkwa" – Signature in pencil on p. [3] – Small pencil drawing of the head of a woman (?) and other small pencil doodles on inside back cover– p. [319].

7 1933
Disney, Walt, 1906-1966 [author]
[Gottfredson, Floyd] [artist & author]
Walt Disney Enterprises [firm]
Mickey Mouse sails for Treasure Island / by Walt Disney. – Racine, WI: Whitman Publishing Company, (c1933, Walt Disney Enterprises, New York, N.Y.) c1933. – 314, i.e., [320] p.: b & w ills.; col. ills. on covers & spine; 11.5 x 9 x 3.5 cm. – (The big little book; 750)

[Copy 1: Notes: "GW30" – Lowery, 1981. – Hard covers & spine. – Publisher's advertisement – p. [316]. – "Delmar" – Written in pencil on p. [3]. – "320 pages" – In red circle on spine].

[Copy 2: Notes: "GW30" – Lowery, 1981. – Hard covers & spine. – Publisher's advertisement – p. [316]. – "Mr. Deeds goes to town; Captain January (Shirley Temple); etc. – Written in pen on pp. [2 & 318]. – Library's copy lacking pp. [3-38 & spine].

8 1933
Disney, Walt, 1901-1966 [author]
[Gottfredson, Floyd] [artist & author]
Walt Disney Studios, Inc. [firm]
Mickey Mouse, the mail pilot / by Walt
Disney. – Racine, WI: Whitman Publishing Company, (c1933, Walt Disney Studios, Inc., New York, N.Y.), c1933. – 296,
i.e., [300] p.: b & w ills.; col. ills. on covers & spine; 11 x 10.5 x 3.5 cm. – (The
big little book; 731)

[Notes: "GW21c" – Lowery 1981. – Soft covers & spine. – "Duane H. Siers" – Stamped on inside front cover. – Illustrated title page. – Publisher's advertisement – p. [298]. – Library's copy lacking pp. [3-4].

8.5 1933
Willard, Frank [artist & author]
Moon Mullins and Kayo / by Frank Willard. – [Cocomalt edition]. – Racine, WI: Whitman Publishing Company, 1933. – [200] p.: b & w ills.; col. ills. on covers; 10.5 x 9 x 2.5 cm. – (The big little book)

[Notes: "GWp13" – Lowery, 1981. – Soft covers & spine. – "Duane H. Siers" – Stamped on head of title page. – Cocomalt advertisements. – pp. [3 & 199-200]. – "Millions gain new strength, energy, vitality – on this delicious food-drink. Cocomalt is accepted by the American Medical Association Committee on Foods. ... It tastes good and *is* good for you! – On back cover. – "Adapted from Moon Mullins and Kayo, #731, i.e., [746]" – Lowery, 1981, p. 104].

(**SEE ALSO** #5 in this checklist.)

9 1933
Enright, W.J. [artist & author]
Once upon a time / by W. J. Enright; with pictures suitable for coloring and crayoning. – Racine, WI: Whitman Publishing Company, (c1933, McClure Newspaper Syndicate, New York City), c1933. – 357, i.e., [360] p.: b & w ills.; col. ills.

on covers & spine [lacking back cover]; 10 x 9 x 4.5 cm. – (The big little book; no. 718)

[Notes: "GW11" – Lowery, 1981. –CONTENTS: Snow White and Rose Red, p. 9; The magic porridge pot, p. 41; Hansel and Grethel, p. 53, i.e., [59]; The cobbler and the brownies, p. 109; Hans in luck, p. 127; Jorinda and Jorindel, p. 157; The three wishes, p. 183; Rumpelstiltzkin, p. 201; The story of Cinderella, p. 227; The hare and the tortoise, p. 283; One eye, two eyes and three eyes, p. 293. – Soft covers & spine. – "Duane H. Siers" – Stamped on p. [3] – Publisher's advertisement. – p. [358] – Color illustrations on covers & spine signed: "J.C.B."].

10 1933
Berndt, 1899-1980
[artist & author]
Smitty: Golden Gloves Tournament / by Walter Berndt. – Racine, WI: Whitman Publishing Company, (c1933, Walter Berndt) c1934. – 282, i.e., [320] p.: b & w ills.; col. ills. on covers & spine; 11.5 x 9.5 x 3.5 cm. – (The big little book; 745)

[Notes: "GW25" – Lowery 1981. – Hard covers & spine. – "Duane H. Siers" – Stamped on inside front cover. – Library's copy lacking pp. [3-4, 283-318].

11 1933
Bennett, Juanita [artist]
Stevenson, Robert Louis, 1850-1894
[author]
The story of Treasure Island / retold from the story by Robert Louis Stevenson; illustrated by Juanita Bennett. – Racine, WI: Whitman Publishing Company, c1933. – 357, i.e., [362] p.: b & w ills.; col. ills. on covers & spine. – 10.5 x 9 x 5 cm. – (The big little book; 720)

[Notes: "GW13" – Lowery, 1981. – Soft covers & spine. – "Treasure Island" – On front cover & spine. – Publisher's advertisement. – p. [358].

#9

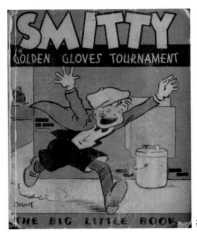

#10

12 1934
Calkins, Dick [artist]
Nowlan, Phil [author]
Buck Rogers in the city below the sea
/ by H. Dick Calkins and Phil Nowlan. –
Racine, WI: Whitman Publishing Com-
pany, (c1934, John F. Dille Co., Chicago,
Ill.), c1934. – 314, i.e., [320] p.: b & w
ills.; col. ills. on covers; 11.5 x 9 x 4 cm.
– (The big little book; 765)

[Notes: "GW43" – Lowery, 1981. – Hard covers & spine. – "Duane H. Siers" – Stamped
on inside front cover. – Publisher's advertisement. – p. [316].

13 1934
Quigley, Robert, 1902- .
[author]
Maynard, Ken [actor]
Laemmle, Carl, 1867-1939 [producer]
Universal Pictures [firm]
**Carl Laemmle presents Ken Maynard
in "Gun justice"** / the story of the Universal Picture based on the screen play
by Robert Quigley. – Racine, WI: Whitman Publishing Company, c1934. – 156,

i.e., [160] p.: b & w photo stills; col. ills.
on covers; 13.5 x 12 x 2.5 cm. – (The
big little book; 776)

[Notes: "GW52a" – Lowery, 1981. – Hard
covers & soft spine. – "Duane H. Siers" –
Stamped on inside front cover. – "Gun justice; featuring Ken Maynard, with Cecilia
Parker, Hooper Atchley, Walter Miller: a
Universal Picture: read the story-then see
the picture" – On front cover].

14 1934
Marsh, Norman
[artist & author]
[Dan Dunn, secret operative 48 / by
Norman Marsh. – Racine, WI: Whitman
Publishing Company, c1934]. – 314, i.e.,
[320] p.: b & w ills.: col. ills. on covers
& spine; 11.5 x 9 x 4 cm. – (The big little book; 1116)

[Notes: "GW66" – Lowery, 1981. – Hard covers & spine. – "Duane H. Siers" – Stamped
on inside front cover. – Publisher's advertisements. – pp. [316-317]. – Library's copy
lacking pp. [3-11] – "Crime never pays" – On
front cover. – "For law and order" – On back
cover].

#11

#14

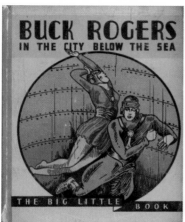

#12

#15

#13

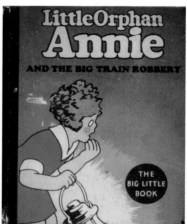

#16

15 1934
Anthony, Edward, 1895- .
[author]
Beatty, Clyde, 1905-1965 [actor]
Laemmle, Carl, 1867-1939 [producer]
Universal Pictures [firm]
Lions and tigers with Clyde Beatty /
with pictures from the Carl Laemmle production, "The Big Cage;" based on the
story, "The Big Cage" by Edward Anthony.
– Racine, WI: Whitman Publishing Company, c1934. – 154, i.e., [160] p.: b & w
photo stills; col. ills. on covers; 13.5 x 12
x 2.5 cm. – (The big little book; 653)

[Notes: "GW1" – Lowery, 1981 – Hard covers
& spine. – "Duane H. Siers" – Stamped on
inside front cover. – Publisher's advertisement – p. [156] – "Carl Laemmle presents:
Lions and tigers, with the sensational dare-
devil, Clyde Beatty / a Universal super special." – On front cover. – "Lions and tigers."
– On spine].

16 1934
Gray, Harold [artist & author]
**Little Orphan Annie and the big train
robbery** / by Harold Gray. – Racine, WI:
Whitman Publishing Company (c1934, by
Harold Gray, Colton-on-Hudson, N.Y.),
c1934. – 294, i.e., [300] p.: b & w ills.;
col. covers & spine; 11.5 x 9 x 4 cm. –
(The big little book; 1140)

[Notes: "GW80a" – Lowery, 1981. – Hard
covers & spine. – "Duane H. Siers" –
Stamped on inside front cover. – Publisher's
advertisements. – pp. [296-297].

17 1934
Gray, Harold, 1894-1968
[artist & author]
[**Little Orphan Annie with the circus** /
by Harold Gray. – Racine, WI: Whitman
Publishing Company, c1934.] – 314, i.e.,
[320] p.: b & w ills.; col. ills. on covers;
11.5 x 9 x 4 cm. – (The big little book;
1103)

[Notes: "GW57" – Lowery, 1981. – Hard covers & spine. – Publisher's advertisements. –
pp. [316]. – Library's copy lacking title page
& pp. [3-6].

18 1934
Hallan, Kenneth [author]
MacDonald, Philip [author]
Ford, John, 1894-1973 [director]
McLaglen, Victor, 1886-1959 [actor]
Karloff, Boris, 1887-1969 [actor]
RKO Pictures [firm]
The lost patrol / starring Victor McLag-
len, Boris Karloff, Wallace Ford, Reginald
Denny, Sammy Stein, Alan Hale; from
the story "Patrol" by Philip MacDonald;
adapted by Kenneth Hallam; directed by
John Ford; Merian C. Cooper, Executive
Producer. – Racine WI: Whitman Publish-
ing Company (Courtesy of A.L. Burt Com-
pany), c1934. – 158, i.e., [160] p.: b & w
photo stills; col. covers & spine; 13.5 x
12 x 2 cm. – (The big little book; 753)

[Notes: "GW32" – Lowery, 1981. – Hard cov-
ers & soft spine. – "Duane H. Siers" –
Stamped on inside front cover. – "Featuring
Victor McLaglen, Boris Karloff...An R.K.O.
Picture" – On front cover. – "160 pages" – In
black circle on spine].

19 1934
McCall, Ted [artist & author]
Men of the Mounted / by Ted McCall. –
Racine, WI: Whitman Publishing Company, (c1933, The Toronto Evening Tele-
gram, Toronto, Ontario), c1934. – 314 p.,
i.e., [320] p.: b & w ills.; col. ills. on covers; 11.5 x 9 x 4 cm. – (The big little
book; 755)

[Notes: "GW34" – Lowery, 1981. – Hard covers
& spine. – "Men of the Mounted: adventures
of the Canadian Royal Mounted" – On front
cover. – Library's copy lacking pp. [315-318].

20 1934
Disney, Walt, 1901-1966 [author]
Gottfredson, Floyd [artist & author]
Mickey Mouse in Blaggard Castle / by
Walt Disney. – Racine, WI: Whitman Pub-
lishing Company, (c1934, Walt Disney
Enterprises, New York, N.Y.) c1934. –
314, i.e., [320] p.: b & w ills.; col. ills. on
covers; 11.5 x 9 x 4 cm. – (The big little
book; [726])

[Notes: "GW20" – Lowery 1981. – Hard covers & spine. – "Duane H. Siers" – Stamped
on inside front cover. – Illustrations by Floyd
Gottfredson. – Lowery 1981. – Library's copy
lacking pp. [3-4, 224-225, 316-318] & spine
and approximately half of the illustrations
are hand-colored with pencil].

21 1934
Alcott, Louisa May, 1832-1888
[author]
Packer, Eleanor Lewis [author]
Levine, Nat, 1899-   . [producer]
Rosen, Phil, 1888-1951 [director]
Mascot Pictures [firm]
**Nat Levine presents: Louisa M.
Alcott's Little Men** / retold by Eleanor
Packer; and illustrated with scenes from
the Mascot Production; starring Ralph
Morgan, Erin O'Brien-Moore, Junior
Durkin, Cora Sue Collins, Phyllis Fraser;
directed by Phil Rosen; Read the story –
see the picture. – Racine, WI: Whitman
Publishing Company, c1934. – 156, i.e.,
[160] p.: b & w photo; col. photos on
covers; 13.5 x 12 x 2.5 cm. – (The big
little book; 1150)

[Notes: "GW89" – Lowery, 1981. – Hard covers & soft spine. – "Duane H. Siers" –
Stamped on inside front cover. – "Cast of
characters" – p. [5]. – Publisher's advertisements, pp. [4] & [158]. – Publisher's advertisements. – p. [4] & [158]. – "Little men"
by Louisa M. Alcott'; "A Mascot Picture: read
the story, see the picture" – On front cover].

22 1934
Arbo, Hal [artist]
Alkire, G.A. [author]
Prairie Bill and the covered wagon /
by G.A. Alkire; illustrated by Hal Arbo. –
Racine, WI: Whitman Publishing Company, c1934. – 378, i.e., [384] p.: b & w
ills.; col. ills. on covers & spine; 11.5 x 9
x 3.5 cm. – (The big little book; 758)

[Notes: "GW37a" – Lowery, 1981. – Hard covers & spine. – Publisher's advertisement, p.
[380].

23 1934
Stevenson, Robert Louis, 1850-
1894 [author]
Packer, Eleanor Lewis [author]
Cooper, Jackie, 1922-   .[actor]
Beery, Wallace [actor]
Fleming, Victor, 1883-1949 [film
director]
Stromberg, Hunt [film producer]
Metro-Goldwyn-Mayer Pictures [firm]
**Robert Louis Stevenson's Treasure
Island** / retold by Eleanor Packer; illus-
trated with scenes from the Metro-Gold-
wyn-Mayer Picture; starring Jackie Coop-
er, Wallace Beery, Lionel Barrymore, Otto
Kruger, Charles "Chic" Sale, Lewis Stone;
directed by Victor Fleming; produced by
Hunt Stromberg. – Racine, WI: Whitman
Publishing Company, c1934.—157, i.e.,
[160] p.: b & w photo; col. photos on
covers; 13.5 x 11.5 x 2.5 cm. – (The big
little book; 1141)

[Notes: "GW 81" – Lowery, 1981. – Hard cov-
ers & soft spine. – "Duane H. Siers" –
Stamped on inside front cover. – Publisher's
advertisement. – p. [158]. – "Jackie Cooper
& Wallace Berry in Treasure Island" & "A
Metro-Goldwyn Mayer Picture; Read the
story, see the picture" – On front cover. –
"Jackie Cooper, Wallace Beery, Lionel
Barrymore, Otto Kruger, Lewis Stone, Charles
"Chic" Sales" – On spine].

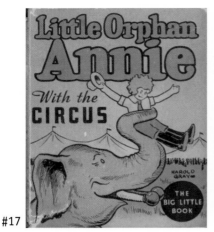

#17

#20

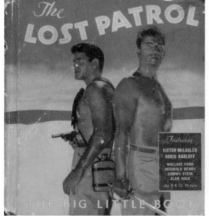

#18

#21

#19

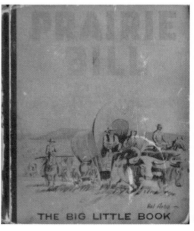

#22

24 1934
Arbo, Hal [artist]
Morgan, Leon [author]
The story of Buffalo Bill / by Leon Morgan; illustrated by Hal Arbo of the W Lazy 5 Ranch. – Racine, WI: Whitman Publishing Company, c1934. – 378, i.e., [384] p.: b & w. ills.; col. ills. on covers and spine; 11.5 x 9.5 x 3.5 cm.. – (The big little book; 713)

[Notes: "GW6" – Lowery, 1981. – Hard covers & spine. – "Duane H. Siers" – Stamped on inside front cover. – Publisher's advertisement – p. [380]. "Buffalo Bill and the Pony Express" – On front cover & spine].

25 1934
Crosby, Percy L. (Percy Leo), 1891-1964 [artist & author]
[The story of Skippy... — Racine, WI: Whitman Publishing Company, c1934]. – 314, i.e., [320] p.: b & w ills.; col. ills. on covers; 11.5 x 9 x 4 cm. – (The big little book; 761)

[Notes: "GW40" – Lowery, 1981. – Hard covers & spine. – "Duane H. Siers" – Stamped on inside front cover. – Publisher's advertisement – p. [316]. – "Skippy, permission, Percy Crosby" – On front cover & spine. – Library's copy lacking pp. [3-77]. – "These stories are based on a selection of Percy Crosby's 'Skippy' Sunday newspaper cartoons"—From RLIN cataloging record].

26 1934
Forrest, Hal [artist & author]
Tailspin Tommy (trade mark): the dirigible flight to the North Pole / By Hal Forrest. – Racine, WI: Whitman Publishing Co., (c1934, Stephen Slesinger, New York, N.Y.), c1934. – [432] p.: b & w ills.; col. ills. on covers & spine; 11.5 x 9 x 4 cm. – (The big little book; 1124)

[Notes: "GW71a" – Lowery, 1981. – Hard covers & spine. – Library's copy lacking pp. [427-430] & spine. – "Miss Thelma Jones" – Signature in ink on p. 3 & 5].

27 1934
Taylor, George R. [artist]
Vale, Richard X. [author]
Tom Beatty, ace of the service / by Richard X. Vale; illustrated by George R. Taylor. – Racine, WI: Whitman Publishing Company, c1934. – 250, i.e., [256] p.: b & w ills.; col. ills. on covers & spine; 14 x 12.5 x 2.5 cm. – (The big little book; 723)

[Notes: "GW17a" – Lowery, 1981.. – Hard covers. – "Duane H. Siers" – Stamped on inside front cover. – "A new story, new thrills, new pictures." – On front cover. – "This book and GW16 were given identical publisher's numbers. GW17a may have been intended to be #733 or #743." – Lowery, 1981, p. 31.]

28 1934
Kurth, Otto [author]
Stallings, Laurence, 1894-   . [photographer]
The World War in photographs: 190 authentic photographs—a pictorial history of the battles in Europe, Asia and Africa, in the air and on the seas / arranged and edited by Otto Kurth; inspired by Laurence Stallings' famous collection of war pictures entitled: "The First World War." – Racine, WI: Whitman Publishing Company, c1934. – [160] p.: [190] b & w photos; b & w photos on covers & spine; 13.5 x 11.5 x 2.5 cm. – (The big little book; 779)

[Notes: "GW54" – Lowery, 1981. – Hard covers & soft spine. – "Duane H. Siers" – Stamped on inside front cover. – "A brief history of the World War (1914-1918)" – p. [6]. – "The cost in men and money." – p. [158]. – "Important events of the World War" – p. [159].

#23

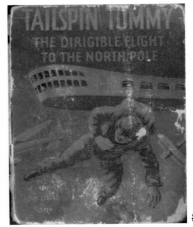

#26

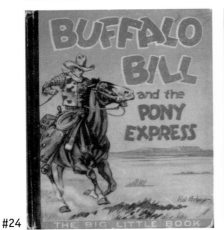

#24

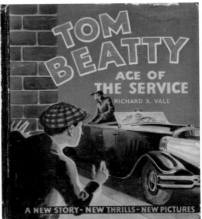

#27

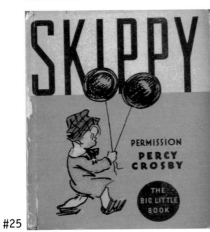

#25

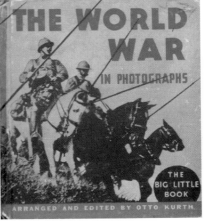

#28

29 1935
[Knight, Clayton] [artist]
Rickenbacker, Eddie, 1890-1973 [author]
Ace Drummond / by Captain Eddie Rickenbacker. – Racine, WI: Whitman Publishing Co. (c1935, by King Features Syndicate, Inc., N.Y.), c1935. – 424. i.e., [432] p.: b & w ills.; col. ills. on covers; 11.5 x 9 x 4 cm. – (The big little book; 1177)

[Notes: "GW114" – Lowery, 1981. – Hard covers & spine. – "Duane H. Siers" – Stamped on inside front cover. – Publisher's advertisements. – pp. [426-428].

#29

30 1935
Link, Stanley [artist & author]
The adventures of Tiny Tim / by Stanley Link. – Racine, WI: Whitman Publishing Company (c1935, Stanley Link, Brooksdale, Ill.), c1935. – 378, i.e., [384] p.: b & w ills.; col. ills. on covers; 11.5 x 9 x 4 cm. – (The big little book; 767)

[Notes: "GW45" – Lowery, 1981. – Hard covers & spine. – "Duane H. Siers" – Stamped on inside front cover. – Publisher's advertisements. – pp. [379-380]. – "From the famous comic strip" – On front cover].

#30

31 1935
Arbo, Hal [artist]
Morgan, Leon [author]
Billy the Kid / by Leon Morgan; with pictures by Hal Arbo of the W Lazy 5 Ranch. – Racine, WI: Whitman Publishing Co., c1935. – 426, i.e., [432] p.: b & w ills.; col. ills. on covers & spine; 11.5 x 9 x 4 cm. – (The big little book; no. 773)

[Notes: "GW50" – Lowery, 1981. – Hard covers & spine. – "Duane H. Siers" – Stamped on inside front cover. – Publisher's advertisement. – p. [328-329].

#31

32 1935
Calkins, Dick [artist]
Nowlan, Phil [author]
Buck Rogers and the Depth Men of Jupiter / written by Phil Nowlan; drawn by Lt. Dick Calkins. – Racine, WI: Whitman Publishing Company (c1935, by John P. Dille Co., Chicago, Ill), c1935. – 424, i.e., [432] p.: b & w ills.; col. ills. on covers & spine; 11.5 x 9 x 4 cm. – (The big little book; 1169)

[Notes: "GW106" – Lowery, 1981. – Hard covers & spine. – "Duane H. Siers" – Stamped on inside front cover. – "Table of contents", p. [7-8]. – Publisher's advertisements. – pp. [426-428] – "25th century A.D." – On front cover. – "Buck Rogers, Wilma, and Doctor Huer drop into the interior depths of the planet Jupiter in a sphereship of impervium metal, where they find the weird Depth Men and other strange creatures." –On back cover].

33 1935
Calkins, Dick [artist]
Nolan, Phil [author]
Buck Rogers, 25th century A.D., and the Doom Comet / written by Phil Nolan; drawn by Lt. Dick Calkins. – Racine, WI: Whitman Publishing Co. (c1935, by John F. Dille Co., Chicago, Ill.), c1935. – 424, i.e., [432] p.: b & w ills.; col. ills. on covers & spine; 11.5 x 9 x 4 cm. – (The big little book; 1178)

[Notes: "GW115" – Lowery, 1981. – Hard covers & spine. – "Duane H. Siers" –Stamped on inside front cover. – Publisher's advertisements. – pp. [426-428]. – "Buck Rogers and the Doom Comet" – On spine. – "From the famous comic strip" – On front cover].]

34 1935
Smith, Sidney [artist & author]
Chester Gump in the city of gold / by Sidney Smith. – Racine, WI: Whitman Publishing Company, (c1935, by Sidney Smith), c1935. – 426, i.e., [432] p.: b &

w ills.; col. ills. on covers; 11.5 x 9 x 4 cm. – (The big little book; 1146)

[Notes: "GW86a" – Lowery, 1981. – Hard covers & spine. – "Duane H. Siers" – Stamped on inside front cover. – Library's copy lacking pp. [3-4], [429-430] & spine].

35 1935
Johnson, Martin, 1884-1937 [artist & author]
Danger trails in Africa / By the famous explorer, Martin Johnson. – Racine, WI: Whitman Publishing Co. (c1935, by Stephen Slesinger, Inc., New York, N.Y.), c1935. – 426, i.e., [432] p.: b & w ills.; col. ills. on covers & spine; 11.5 x 9 x 4 cm. – (The big little book; 1151)

[Notes: "GW90" – Lowery, 1981. – Hard covers & spine. – "Table of contents" – p. [7] – Publisher's advertisements. – pp. [427-429]. – "By the famous explorer Martin Johnson" – On front cover].

36 1935
Gould, Chester [artist & author]
Dick Tracy on the trail of Larceny Lu / by Chester Gould. – Racine, WI: Whitman Publishing Company (c1935, by Chester Gould), 1935. – 424, i.e., [432] p.: b & w ill.; col. ills. on covers & spine; 11.5 x 9 x 4 cm. – (The big little book; 1170)

[Copy 1: Notes: "GW107" – Lowery, 1981. – Hard covers & spine. – "Table of contents" – p. [7-8] – Publisher's advertisements, pp. [426-428] – "Hal," Junior Tracy thought with a thrill. "There's that woman again who's been following me around. Wonder what she's after?" – On front cover].

[Copy 2: Notes: "GW107" – Lowery, 1981. – Hard covers & spine. – "Table of contents" – p. [7-8] – Publisher's advertisements, pp. [426-428] – "Hal," Junior Tracy thought with a thrill. "There's that woman again who's been following me around. Wonder what she's after?" – On front cover. – Library's copy lacking pp. [3-9, 429-430], spine and back cover].

37 1935
Beroth, I.A. [artist]
Martinek, Frank V. [author]
Don Winslow, U.S.N. (trade mark) / by
Lieut.-Comdr. Frank V. Martinek, U.S.N.R.
– Racine, WI: Whitman Publishing Com-
pany (c1935, by Stephen Slesinger, Inc.,
New York, N.Y.), c1935. – 427, i.e., [432]
p.: b & w ills.; col. ills. on covers & spine;
11.5 x 9 x 4 cm. – (The big little book ;
1107)

[Notes: "GW61a" – Lowery, 1981. – Hard cov-
ers & spine. – "Table of contents"—p. [7-8].
– Publisher's advertisements. – pp. [428-429].
– "Lieutenant Commander Don Winslow,
U.S.N." – On front cover. – "I.A. Beroth,
artist" – Lowery, 1981, p. 47].

38 1935
Raymond, Alex [artist &
author]
**Flash Gordon and the tournaments of
Mongo** / by Alex Raymond. – Racine, WI:
Whitman Publishing Co. (c1935, by King
Features Syndicate, Inc., New York, N.Y.),
c1935. – 425, i.e., [432] p.: b & w ills.;
col. ills on covers; 11.5 x 9 x 4 cm. – (The
big little book; 1171)

[Notes: "GW108" – Lowery, 1981. – Hard covers & spine. – "Duane H. Siers" – Stamped on
inside front cover. – Illustrated title page. –
"Table of contents", p. [7]. – Publisher's
advertisements. – pp. [426-428] – "From the
famous comic strip" – On cover].

39 1935
Cravath, Glen [artist & author]
**Frank Buck presents Ted Towers, ani-
mal master** / by Glen Cravath. – Racine,
WI: Whitman Publishing Co. (c1935, by
King Features Syndicate, Inc., New York,
N.Y.), c1935. – 422, i.e., [432] p.: b & w
ills.; col. ills. on covers & spine; 11.5 x 9
x 4 cm. – (The big little book; 1175)

[Notes: "GW112" – Lowery, 1981. – Hard covers & spine. – Library's copy lacking pp. [2-3].
– "Table of contents", p. 7. – Publisher's
advertisements. – pp. [424-427]. – "From the
famous comic strip" – On cover.]

40 1935
Gray, Harold, 1894-1968
[artist & author]
**Little Orphan Annie and Punjab the
wizard** / by Harold Gray.—Racine, WI:
Whitman Publishing Company (c,1935,
by Harold Gray, Colton-on-Hudson, N.Y.),
c1935. – 424, i.e., [432] p.: b & w ills.;
col. ills. on covers; 11.5 x 9 x 4 cm. –
(The big little book; 1162)

[Notes: "GW100" – Lowery, 1981. – Hard covers & spine. – "Duane H. Siers" – Stamped on
inside front cover. – "Table of contents", p.
[7]. – Lacking pp. [3-4 & 427-430] –
Publisher's advertisements. – pp. [426-428]. –
"From comic strip: early 1935 to May 6,
1935." – Lowery, 1981].

41 1935
Arbo, Hal [artist]
Trendle, George W. [author]
Striker, Fran, 1903-1962 [author]
The Lone Ranger and his horse Silver
/ illustrated by Hal Arbo; based on the
famous radio program. – Racine, WI:
Whitman Publishing Company, c1935. –
424, i.e., [432] p.: b & w ills.; col. ills. on
front cover & spine; col. photo on back
cover; 11.5 x 9 x 4 cm. – (The big little
book; 1181)

[Notes: "GW 118" – Lowery, 1981. – Hard
covers & spine. – "Duane H. Siers" – Stamped
on inside front cover. – "Table of contents" –
pp. [7-8]. – Publisher's advertisements. – pp.
[426-428]. – Library's copy lacking pp. [3-4].
– "Created by Trendle and Striker" – Lowery,
1981, p. 61].

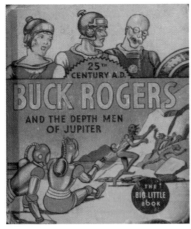

#32

#35

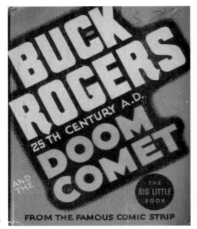

#33

#36

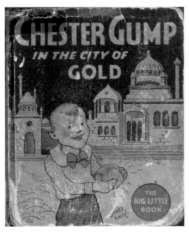

#34

#37

#38

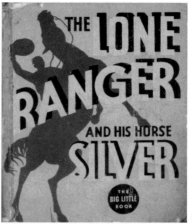

#41

#39

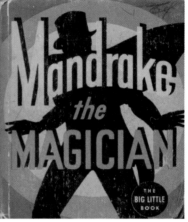

#42

#40

#43

42 1935
Davis, Phil, 1906-1964 [artist]
Falk, Lee [author]
Mandrake the magician / by Lee Falk and Phil Davis. – Racine, WI: Whitman Publishing Co. (c1935, by King Features Syndicate, Inc., New York, N.Y.), c1935. – 424. i.e., [432] p.: b & w ills.; col. ills. on covers & spine: 11.5 x 9.5 x 4 cm. – (The big little book; 1167)

[Notes: "GW104" – Lowery, 1981. – Hard covers & spine. – "Duane H. Siers" – Stamped on inside front cover. – "Table of Contents", p. [7]. – Publisher's advertisements, pp. [426-428].

43 1935
Disney, Walt, 1901-1966 [author]
[Gottfredson, Floyd] [artist]
Walt Disney Enterprises, Inc. [firm]
Mickey Mouse and Bobo the elephant / by Walt Disney. – Racine, WI: Whitman Publishing Co. (c1935, Walt Disney Enterprises, Inc., New York, N.Y.), c1935. – 424, i.e., [432] p.: b & w ills.; col. ills. on covers & spine; 11.5 x 9 .x 4 cm. – (The big little book; 1160)

[Notes: "GW98" – Lowery, 1981. – Hard covers & spine. – "Table of contents" – p. [7]. – "Duane H. Siers" – Stamped on inside front cover. – Lacking back cover and pp. [3-4], [427-432]. – Publisher's advertisement, – p. [426].

44 1935
Disney, Walt, 1901-1966 [author]
Gottfredson, Floyd [artist & author]
Mickey Mouse and the Bat Bandit / by Walt Disney. – Racine, WI: Whitman Publishing Co. (c1935, Walt Disney Enterprises, Inc., New York, N.Y.), c1935. – 426, i.e., [432] p.: b & w ills.; col. ills. on covers & spine; 11.5 x 9 x 4 cm. – (The big little book; 1153)

[Notes: "GW92a" – Lowery, 1981. – Hard covers & spine. – Publisher's advertisements. – pp. [2-4], [428-431]. – "Floyd Gottfredson, artist & author" – Lowery, 1981, p. 55].

45 1935
Sullivan, Eddie [artist]
Schmidt, Charlie [author]
Radio patrol / by Eddie Sullivan and Charlie Schmidt. – Racine, WI: Whitman Publishing Company (c1935, by King Features Syndicate, Inc., Great Britain), c1935. – 424, i.e., [432] p.: b & w ills.; col. ills. on covers & spine; 11.5 x 9.5 x 4 cm. – (The big little book; 1142)

[Notes: "GW82" – Lowery, 1981. – Hard covers & spine. – "Duane H. Siers" – Stamped on inside front cover. – Publisher's advertisements. – pp. [426-429].

46 1935
Gould, Will [artist & author]
Red Barry, ace-detective / by Will Gould. – Racine, WI: Whitman Publishing Company (c1935, King Features Syndicate, Inc., New York, N.Y.), c1935. – 426, i.e., [432] p.: b & w ills.; col. ills. on covers & spine; 11.5 x 9 x 4 cm. – (The big little book; 1157)

[Notes: "GW96" – Lowery, 1981. – Hard covers & spine. – Table of Contents, p. [7]. – Publisher's advertisements. – pp. [427-429]. – "Red Barry, hero of the hour." – On spine].

47 1935
Packer, Eleanor Lewis [author]
Hoyt, Vance Joseph [author]
Parker, Jean [actress]
Franklin, Chester M. [director]
Considine, John W. [producer]
Metro-Goldwyn-Mayer Pictures [firm]
Sequoia, the story of a strange friendship between a mountain lion and a deer / retold by Eleanor Packer; and illustrated with scenes from the Metro-

Goldwyn-Mayer Production; based on the novel "Malibu," by Vance Hoyt; directed by Chester M. Franklin; produced by John W. Considine, Jr.; featuring Jean Parker, Samuel S. Hinds, Ben Hall, Willie Fung, Russell Hardie, Paul Hurst, Harry Lowe, Jr.; read the book – see the picture. – Racine, WI: Whitman Publishing Company, c1935. – 156, i.e., [160] p.: b & w. photo; col. photos on covers; 13.5 x 12 x 2.5 cm. – (The big little book; 1161)

[Notes: "GW99" – Lowery, 1981. – Hard covers & soft spine. – "Duane H. Siers" – Stamped on inside front cover. – "Read the book – see the picture" – On front cover. – Publisher's advertisements. – pp. [2 & 158-159]. – "Thrilling wild amimal [i.e., animal] adventures" – On cover. – Colored photograph of Gato, the mountain lion and Malibu, the deer on back cover].

48 1935
Forrest, Hal [artist & author]
Tailspin Tommy (trade mark) : hunting for pirate gold / by Hal Forrest. – Racine, WI: Whitman Publishing Co. (c1935, by Stephen Slesinger, Inc., New York, N.Y.), c1935. – 424, i.e., [432] p.: b & w ills.; col. ills. on covers & spine; 11.5 x 9 x 4 cm. – (The big little book; 1172)

[Notes: "GW109" – Lowery, 1981. – Hard covers & spine. – "Duane H. Siers" – Stamped on inside front cover. – "Table of contents" – p. [7]. – Publisher's advertisements. – pp. [426-429].

49 1935
Rister, Claude [author]
Packer, Eleanor Lewis [author]
McCoy, Tim [actor]
Selman, David [director]
Columbia Pictures [firm]
Tim McCoy in The Prescott Kid / retold by Eleanor Packer; from the Columbia Motion Picture starring Tim McCoy; story by Claude Rister; directed by David Selman; with a cast including: Sheila Mannors, Alden Chase, Albert J. Smith, Joseph Sauers, Hooper Atchley, Harry Todd; read the story, see the picture. – Racine, WI: Whitman Publishing Company, c1935. – 156, i.e., [160] p.: b & w photos; col. photos on covers & spine; 13.5 x 12 x 2.5 cm. – (The big little book; 1152)

[Notes: "GW91" – Lowery, 1981. – Hard covers & soft spine. – "Duane H. Siers" – Stamped on inside front cover. – Publishers advertisements. – p. [2] & [159]. – "Tim McCoy in The Prescott Kid, a Columbia Picture. Tim McCoy fights his way through another thrill-packed adventure tale. Nerve-tingling action! A red-blooded, heart-pounding drama of the Old West. . . . Read the book, see the picture." – On front cover].

50 1935
Arbo, Hal [artist]
Morgan, Leon [author]
Tom Mix in The fighting cowboy / story by Leon Morgan; pictures by Hal Arbo; "Tom Mix" trade mark. – Racine, WI: Whitman Publishing Company (c1935, by Stephen Slesinger, Inc., N.Y.), c1935 – 426, i.e., [432] p. : b & w ills.; col. ills. on covers; 11.5 x 9 x 4 cm. – (The big little book; 1144)

[Notes: "GW84a" – Lowery, 1981. – Hard covers & spine. – "Duane H. Siers" – Stamped on inside front cover. – "Table of contents" – pp. [7-8]. – Publisher's advertisements. – pp. [428-429].

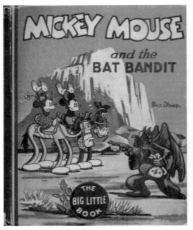

#44

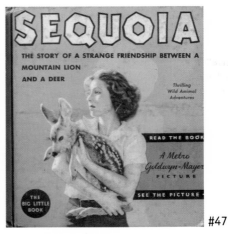

#47

#45

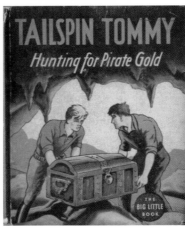

#48

#46

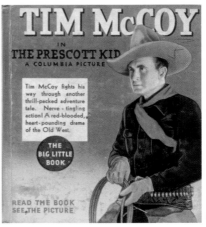

#49

51 1935
Parker, Eleanor Lewis [author]
Twentieth Century-Fox [firm]
[Twentieth Century-Fox presents: This is the life, starring Jane Withers / story retold from the motion picture by Eleanor Parker. – Racine, WI: Whitman Publishing Company, c1935]. – 236, i.e., [240] p.: b & w photos; col. photos on covers; 11.5 x 9 x 4 cm. – (The big little book; 1179)

[Notes: "GW116" – Lowery, 1981. – Hard covers & soft spine. – "Duane H. Siers" – Stamped on red-bordered label glued to inside front cover. – Publishers advertisements. – p. [238]. – Library's copy lacking pp. [3-4]. – "Twentieth Century-Fox presents Jane Withers in This is the life. Read the book, see the picture" – On front cover].

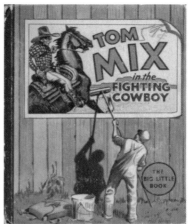

#50

52 1935
Warner Brothers Pictures, Inc. [firm]
Vitaphone Corporation [firm]
Warner Bros. Pictures, Inc. and the Vitaphone Corp'n present: Little big shot / with Sybil Jason, Glenda Farrell, Robert Armstrong, Edward Everett Horton; directed by Michael Curtiz: A Warner Bros. Production Corp'n Picture. – Racine, WI: Whitman Publishing Co., c1935. – [240] p.: b & w photos; col. photos on covers & spine; 11.5 x 9 x 3.5 cm. – (The big little book; 1149)

[Notes: "GW88" – Lowery, 1981. – Hard covers & spine. – Library's copy lacking pp. [237-238]. – "Sybil Jason in Little big shot: a Warner Bros. Picture: Read the book, see the picture" – On front cover.]

#51

53 1936
Orr, Martha [artist & author]
Apple Mary and Dennie foil the swindlers / by Martha Orr; based on the famous newspaper strip. – Racine, WI:

#52

Whitman Publishing Company (c1936, by Publishers Syndicate; licensed by Stephen Slesinger, Inc., New York, N.Y.), c1936. – 424, i.e., [432] p.: b & w ills.; col. ills. on covers & spine; 11.5 x 9 x 4 cm. – (The big little book; 1130)

[Notes: "GW159" – Lowery, 1981. – Hard covers & spine. – "Table of contents" – p. [7]. – Publisher's advertisements. – pp. [426-428]. – Library's copy lacking pp. [9-10].

54 1936
Arbo, Hal [artist]
Maple, Peter K. [author]
The Arizona Kid on the bandit trail / by Peter K. Maple. – Racine, WI: Whitman Publishing Co., c1936. –424, i.e., [432] p.: b & w ills.; col. ills. on covers & spine; 11.5 x 9 x 4 cm. – (The big little book; 1192)

[Notes: "GW 129" – Lowery, 1981. – Hard covers & spine. – "Duane H. Siers" – Stamped on inside front cover. – "Table of contents" – p. [7]. – Publisher's advertisements. – pp. [425-427]. – Library's copy lacking pp. [3-4 & 428-429]. – "Hal Arbo, artist" – Lowery, 1981, . 63].

55 1936
McManus, George [artist & author]
Bringing up father / by George McManus; a King Features Comic. – Racine, WI: Whitman Publishing Co. (c1936, King Features Syndicate, Inc., New York, N.Y.), c1936. – 424, i.e., [432] p.: b & w ills.; col. ills. on covers; 11.5 x 9.5 x 4 cm. – (The big little book; 1133)

[Notes: GW76" – Lowery, 1981. – Hard covers & spine. – "Duane H. Siers" – Stamped on inside front cover. – Publisher's advertisement. – pp. [426-428]. – "From the famous comic strip." – On front cover].

56 1936
Arbo, Hal [artist]
Wilson, Buck, 1899- . [pseudonym for Gaylord Du Bois]
Buffalo Bill plays a lone hand / By Buck Wilson [pseudonym]; illustrated by Hal Arbo. – Racine, WI: Whitman Publishing Co., c1936. – 424, i.e., [432] p.: b & w ills.; col. ills. on covers & spine; 11.5 x 9 x 4 cm. – (The big little book; 1194)

[Notes: "GW 131" – Lowery, 1981. – Hard covers & spine. – "Table of contents" – p. [7]. – Publisher's advertisements. – pp. [426-428].

57 1936
Gould, Chester [artist & author]
Dick Tracy and the Racketeer Gang / by Chester Gould. – Racine, WI: Whitman Publishing Co. (c1936, by Chester Gould), c1936. – 424, i.e., [432] p.: b & w ills.; col. ills. on covers & spine; 11.5 x 9 x. 4 cm. – (The big little book; 1112)

[Notes: "GW145" – Lowery, 1981. – Hard covers & spine. – "Table of contents" – p. [7]. – Publisher's advertisements. – pp. [426-428]. – "Based on the famous detective strip" – On spine. – "Watchfully waiting, detective Dick Tracy saw four dark figures leave – "something is up!" he thought, and immediately the law went into action." – On back cover].

58 1936
Raymond, Alex, 1909-1956 [artist & author]
Flash Gordon and the Witch Queen of Mongo / by Alex Raymond; based on the famous adventure strip. – Racine, WI: Whitman Publishing Co. (c1936, by King Features Syndicate, Inc., New York, N.Y.), c1936. – 424, i.e., [432] p.: b & w ills.; col. ills. on covers & spine; 11.5 x 9 x 4 cm. – (The big little book; 1190)

[Notes: "GW127" – Lowery, 1981. – Hard covers & spine. – "Duane H. Siers" – Stamped on inside front cover. – "Table of contents" – p. [7]. – Publisher's advertisements. – pp. [426-428].

59 1936
Lee, Dougal [artist & author]
Flying the Sky Clipper with Winsie Atkins / by Dougal Lee. – Racine, WI: Whitman Publishing Co., c1936. – 424, i.e., [432] p.: b & w ills.; col. ills. on covers & spine; 11.5 x 9 x 4 cm. – (The big little book; 1108)

[Notes: "GW142" – Lowery, 1981. – Hard covers & spine. – "Table of Contents" – p. [7]. – "Duane H. Siers" – Stamped on inside front cover. – Publisher's advertisements. –pp. [426-428]. – Library's copy lacking pp. [3-4].

60 1936
Clark, George [artist]
Hanlon, Lou [author]
The G-Man on the crime trail / by George Clark and Lou Hanlon. – Racine, WI: Whitman Publishing Co. (c1936, by the Daily Mirror, New York, N.Y.), c1936. – 424, i.e., [432] p.: b & w ills.; col. ills. on covers; 11.5 x 9 x 4 cm. – (The big little book; 1118)

[Notes: "GW151" – Lowery, 1981. – Hard covers & soft spine. – "Duane H. Siers" – Stamped on small red-bordered label glued to inside front cover. – "Table of contents" – p. [7]. – Publisher's announcements. – pp. [426-428].

61 1936
G-Man vs. the Red X. – Racine, WI: Whitman Publishing Co. (c1936 by Stephen Slesinger, New York, N.Y.), c1936. – 424, i.e., [432] p.: b & w ills.; col. ills. on covers. – 11.5 x 9 x 4 cm. – (The big little book; 1147)

[Notes: "GW167" – Lowery, 1981. – Hard covers & spine. – "Duane H. Siers" – Stamped on inside front cover. – "Table of contents" – p. [7]. – Publisher's adver-

tisements. – pp. [425-427]. – "Who is the mysterious Red X?" – On back cover].

62 1936
Knight, Clayton, 1891-1969 [artist]
Rickenbacker, Eddie, 1890-1973 [author]
Hall of Fame of the Air / by Capt. Eddie Rickenbacker; with drawings by Clayton Knight. – Racine, WI: Whitman Publishing Co. (c1936, by King Features Syndicate, Inc., New York, N.Y.), c.1936. – 423, i.e., [432] p.: b & w ills.; col. ills. on covers & spine; 11.5 x 9 x 4 cm. – (The big little book; 1159)

[Notes: "GW171" – Lowery, 1981. – Hard covers & spine. – "Table of contents", p. [6-7]. – Publisher's advertisements. – pp. [424-427]. – "From the famous cartoon strip" – On front cover. – Library's copy lacking pp. [3-4]. – "John Peacock" – Signature in pencil on inside front cover].

63 1936
Moore, Willfred G. [artist]
Burtt, Robert M. [author]
Jimmie Allen and the airmail robbery / by Capt. Willfred G. Moore and Lt. Robert M. Burtt; based on the famous series of radio broadcasts: "The air adventures of Jimmie Allen." – Racine, WI: Whitman Publishing Company (c1936, by Willfred G. Moore and Robert M. Burtt), c1936. – 424, i.e., [432] p.: b & w ills.; col. ills. on covers & spine; 11.5 x 9 x 4 cm. – (The big little book; 1143)

[Notes: "GW165" – Lowery, 1981. – Hard covers & spine. – "Table of contents" – p. [7-8]. – Publisher's advertisements. – pp. [426-428]. – "Jimmy Allen in the airmail robbery" – On front cover].

#53

#56

#54

#57

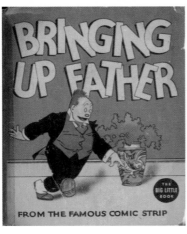

#55

#58

#59

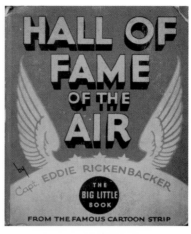

#62

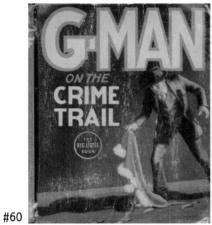

#60

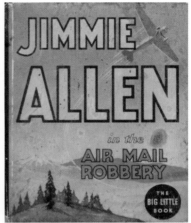

#63

#61

#64

64 1936
Capp, Al, 1909-   .
[artist & author]
Li'l Abner in New York / by Al Capp;
based on the famous comic strip. –
Racine, WI: Whitman Publishing Co.
(c1936, by United Feature Syndicate,
Inc., licensed by Stephen Slesinger, Inc,
New York, N.Y.), c1936. – 424, i.e., [432]
p.: b & w ills.; col. ills. on covers & spine;
11.5 x 9 x 4 cm. – (The big little book;
1198)

[Notes: "GW135" – Lowery, 1981. – Hard covers & spine. – "Belongs [to] Genevieve Wood" – Signature in pencil on p. [3]. – "Table of contents: — p. [7] – Publisher's advertisements. – pp. 425-428].

65 1936
Walsh, Brandon [artist & author]
[**Little Annie Rooney and the orphan house** / based on the comic strip by Brandon Walsh. – Racine, WI: Whitman Publishing Company, 1936]. – 424, i.e., [432] p.: b & w ills.; col. ills. on covers & spine; 11.5 x 9 x 4 cm. – (The big little book; 1117)

[Notes: "GW150" – Lowery, 1981. – Hard covers & spine. – "Duane H. Siers" – Stamped on inside front cover. – "Table of contents" – p. [7]. – Publisher's advertisements. – pp. [426-428]. – Library's copy lacking pp. [3-6].

66 1936
Cory, Fanny Y. [artist & author]
Little Miss Muffet / by Fanny Y. Cory; based on the famous comic strip. – Racine, WI: Whitman Publishing Co. (c1936, by King Features Syndicate, Inc., Great Britain), c1936 – 424, i.e., [432] p.: b & w ills.; col. ills. on covers & spine; 11.5 x 9 x 4 cm. – (The big little book; 1120)

[Notes: "GW152" – Lowery, 1981. – Hard covers & spine. – "Duane H. Siers" – Stamped on

inside front cover. – "Table of contents" – p. [7]. – Publisher's advertisements. – pp. [426-428]. – "Based on the famous comic strip" – On front cover].

67 1936
Disney, Walt, 1901-1966 [author]
Gottfredson, Floyd [artist & author]
Walt Disney Enterprises [firm]
Mickey Mouse and Pluto the racer / by Walt Disney. – Racine, WI: Whitman Publishing Co. (c1936, Walt Disney Enterprises, Hollywood, Calif), c1936. – 424, i.e., [432] p.: b & w ills.; col. ills. on covers & spine; 11.5 x 9 x 4 cm. – (The big little book; 1128)

[Notes: "GW157" – Lowery, 1981. – Hard covers & spine. – "Table of Contents" – p. [7]. – "Duane H. Siers" – Stamped on inside front cover. – Publisher's advertisements. – pp. [426-429]. – "Floyd Gottfredson, artist & author" – Lowery, 1981, p. 70].

68 1936
Packer, Eleanor Lewis [author]
DeMille, Cecil B., 1881-1959 (Cecil Blount) [director]
Cooper, Gary, 1901-1961 [actor]
Arthur, Jean, 1905-   . [actress]
Paramount Pictures [firm]
The Plainsman / retold by Eleanor Packer from the Paramount Motion Picture starring Gary Cooper and Jean Arthur; directed and produced by Cecil B. DeMille; with a cast including James Ellison, Charles Bickford, Helen Burgess, Porter Hall, Paul Harvey, John Miljan; read the book – see the picture. – Racine, WI: Whitman Publishing Co., c1936. – [240] p.: b & w photo; col. photos on covers; 11.5 x 9.5 x 4 cm. – (The big little book; 1123)

[Notes: "GW 153" – Lowery, 1981. – Hard covers & spine. – "Duane H. Siers" – Stamped on inside front cover. – Library's copy lacking pp.

#65

#66

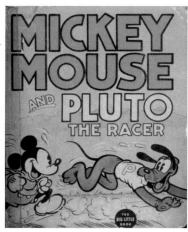

#67

[237-238]. – "Paramount Pictures presents The Plainsman, starring Gary Cooper and Jean Arthur; directed by Cecil B. DeMille: read the book – see the picture." – On front cover. – "Follow the adventures of Buffalo Bill Cody, Wild Bill Hickok, General Custer, Calamity Jane in this fact action motion-picture story of the Old West." – On back cover].

69 1936
Segar, E.C., 1894-1938 (Elzie Crisler) [artist & author]
Popeye the Sailor sees the sea: an original story about the star of Thimble Theatre / by Segar. – Racine, WI: Whitman Publishing Company (c1936, by King Features Syndicate, Inc., New York, N.Y.), c1936. – 424, i.e., [432] p.: b & w ills.; col. ills. on covers & spine; 11.5 x 9 x 4 cm. – (The big little book; 1163)

[Notes: "GW172" – Lowery, 1981. – Hard covers & spine. – "Table of Contents" – p. [7]. – "Popeye sees the sea" – On cover & spine. – Publisher's advertisements. – pp. [426-428].

70 1936
Maxon, Rex [artist]
Burroughs, Edgar Rice, 1875-1950 [author]
The return of Tarzan / by Edgar Rice Burroughs. – Racine, WI: Whitman Publishing Co. (c1936, by Edgar Rice Burroughs, Inc., Tarzana, Calif.), c1936. – 424, i.e, [432] p.: b & w ills.; col. ills. on covers & spine; 11.5 x 9 x 4 cm. – (The big little book; 1102)

[Notes: "GW137" – Lowery, 1981. – Hard covers & spine. – "Table of Contents" – p. [7]. – Publisher's advertisements. – pp. [426-429]. – "Rex Maxon, artist" – Lowery, 1981, p. 66]

71 1936
Vallely, Henry E. [artist]
Engle, William [author]
S O S Coast Guard / Story by William
Engle; illustrations by Henry E. Vallely. –
Racine, WI: Whitman Publishing Co.
(c1936, by Stephen Slesinger, New York,
N.Y.), c1936. – 424, i.e., [432] p.: b & w
ills.; col. ills. on covers & spine; 11.5 x 9
x 4 cm. – (The big little book; 1191)

[Notes: "GW128" – Lowery, 1981. – Hard covers & soft spine. – "Table of contents" – p. [7-8]. – Publisher's advertisements. – pp. [426-428].

72 1936
Raymond, Alex [artist]
Flanders, Charles [author]
Secret Agent X-9 / by Charles Flanders.
– Racine, WI: Whitman Publishing Co.
(c1936, by King Features Syndicate, Inc.,
New York, N.Y.), c1936. – 424, i.e., [432]
p.: b & w ills.; col. ills. on covers & spine;
11.5 x 9 x 4 cm. – (The big little book;
1144)

[Notes: "GW166" – Lowery, 1981. – Hard covers & soft spine. – "Duane H. Siers" – Stamped on inside front cover. – "Table of contents" – p. [7]. – Publisher's advertisements. – pp. [426-429]. – "Based on the famous detective strip." – On front cover. – "Alex Raymond, artist" – Lowery, 1981, p. 72].

73 1936
Cowen, Morton H. [artist]
Arbo, Hal [artist]
Sombrero Pete. – Racine, WI: Whitman
Publishing Co., c1936. – 422, i.e., [432]
p.: b & w ills.; col. ills on covers & spine;
11.5 x 9.5 x 4 cm. – (The big little book;
1136)

[Notes: "GW161" – Lowery, 1981. – Hard covers & spine. – "Duane H. Siers" – Stamped on inside front cover. – Illustrated title page. –

"Table of contents", pp. [6-7]. – Library's copy
lacking pp. [3-4]. – Publisher's advertisements. – pp. [424-427]. – "Cover illustration
by Hal Arbo" – Lowery, 1981, p. 71. – "Morton
H. Cowen, artist" – Lowery, 1981, p. 71].

74 1936
Stevenson, Robert Louis,
1850-1894 [author]
The spy. – Racine, WI: Whitman Publishing Company, c1936. – 295, i.e., [300]
p.: b & w ills.; col. ills on covers & spine;
11.5 x 9.5 x 3.5 cm. – (The big little
book; 768)

[Notes: "GW46" – Lowery, 1981. – Hard covers & spine. – "Duane H. Siers" – Stamped on inside front cover. – Publisher's advertisement. – p. [296-297]– "Adapted from Robert Louis Stevenson" – Lowery, 1981, p. 39].

75 1936
Burroughs, Edgar Rice,
1875-1950 [author]
Weissmuller, Johnny [actor]
O'Sullivan, Maureen. 1911-   . [actress]
Metro-Goldwyn-Mayer [firm]
**[Tarzan escapes: a new story of Tarzan
of the apes** / illustrated with scenes
from the Metro-Goldwyn-Mayer production starring Johnny Weissmuller [and]
Maureen O'Sullivan. – Racine, WI: Whitman Publishing Company, c1936]. – 234,
i.e., [240] p.: b & w photos; col. photos
on covers; 11.5 x 9 x 4 cm. (The big little book; 1182)

[Notes: "GW119" – Lowery, 1981. – Hard covers & spine. – "Duane H. Siers" – Stamped on inside front cover. – Publisher's advertisements – p. [236-237]. – Library's copy lacking pp. [3-16] – "Metro-Goldwyn-Mayer Picture. Read the book, see the picture" – On front cover. – "Not ... authored by Mr. Burroughs": Heins, H.H., A golden anniversary bibliography of Edgar Rice Burroughs, p. 85].

76 1936
Arbo, Hal [artist]
Morgan, Leon [author]
The Texas Ranger on the trail of the Dog Town rustlers / by Leon Morgan; illustrated by Hal Arbo of the W Lazy 5 Ranch. – Racine, WI: Whitman Publishing Co., c1936. – 424, i.e., [432] p.: b & w ills.; col. ills. on covers & spine; 11.5 x 9 x 4 cm. – (The big little book; 1135)

[Notes: "GW160" – Lowery, 1981. – Hard covers & spine. – "Table of contents" – p. [7]. – Publisher's advertisements. – pp. [426-428]. – "The Texas Ranger" – On front cover & spine].

77 1936
Packer, Eleanor Lewis [author]
Columbia Pictures [firm]
[Tim McCoy in The Westerner / by Eleanor Packer. – Racine, WI: Whitman Publishing Company, c1936.] – 236, i.e., [240] p.: b & w photos; col. photos on covers & spine; 11.5 x 9 x 4 cm. – (The big little book; 1193)

[Notes: "GW130" – Lowery, 1981. – Hard covers & spine. – "Duane H. Siers" – Stamped on inside front cover. – Library's copy lacking pp. [3-4, 237-238]. – "A Columbia Picture. See the picture —- read the story" – On front cover].

78 1936
Carne, Don [author]
Uncle Don's strange adventures / by Uncle Don Carney; a story based on "Uncle Don's" famous radio broadcasts, featuring Lanny and Jed Blaine in the exciting adventure with the Mystery Cruiser Q-16. – Racine, WI: Whitman Publishing Company (c1936, Don Carney, New York, N.Y., licensed by Stephen Slesinger, Inc., N.Y.), c1936. – 294, i.e., [300] p.: b & w ills.; col. ills. on covers; 11.5 x 9 x 3.5 cm. – (The big little book; 1114)

[Notes: "GW147" – Lowery, 1981. – Hard covers & spine. – "Duane H. Siers" – Stamped on small red-bordered label glued to inside front cover. – Publisher's advertisements. – pp. [296-298]. – "Uncle Don Carney, famous radio star" – Small photo portrait on front cover.]

79 1936
Smith, Mark [author]
With Mac of the Marines in Africa / by Mark Smith. – Racine, WI: Whitman Publishing Co. (c1936, by Stephen Slesinger, New York, N.Y.), c1936. – 424, i.e., [432] p.: b & w ills.; col. ills. on covers & spine; 11.5 x 9 x 4 cm. – (The big little book; 1189)

[Notes: "GW126" – Lowery, 1981. – Hard covers & spine. – "Duane H. Siers" – Stamped on inside front cover. – "Table of contents" – p. [7-8]. – Publisher's advertisements. – pp. [426-428]. – "Mac of the Marines in Africa" – On front cover & spine. – Library's copy lacking pp. [429-430].

80 1937
[Maxon, Rex] [artist]
Burroughs, Edgar Rice, 1875-1950 [author]
The beasts of Tarzan / by Edgar Rice Burroughs. – Racine, WI: Whitman Publishing Company (c1937, by Edgar Rice Burroughs, Inc., Tarzana, Calif.), c1937. – 424, i.e., [432] p.: b & w ills.; col. ills. on covers; 11.5 x 9 x 4 cm. – (The big little book; 1410)

[Notes: "GW193" – Lowery, 1981. – Hard covers & spine. – "Duane H. Siers" – Stamped on inside front cover. – "Table of contents" – p. [7]. – Publisher's advertisements. – pp. [426-428].

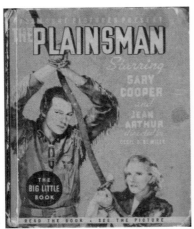

#68

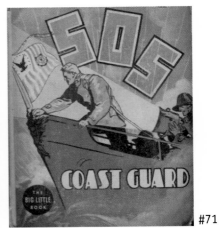

#71

#69

#72

#70

#73

#74

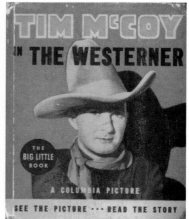

#77

#75

#78

#76

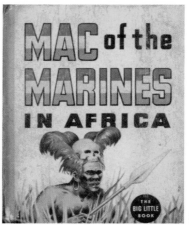

#79

81
1937
Maple, Peter K. [author]

Vallely, Henry E. [cover artist]

Bob Stone, the young detective / story by Peter K. Maple; based on "Picture Crimes"; the stories, names, characters, incidents, and institutions portrayed in this book are fictitious. No identification with actual persons living or deceased is intended or should be inferred. All pictures are posed. – Racine, WI: Whitman Publishing Company (c1937, by Chester Weil), c1937. – 237, i.e., [240] p.; b & w photos; col. ills. on covers & spine; 11.5 x 9 x 4 cm. – (The big little book; 1432)

[Notes: "GW213" – Lowery, 1981. – Hard covers & spine. – "Duane H. Siers" – Stamped on inside front cover. – "Table of contents" – p. [4]. – Publisher's advertisements. – p. [238]. – "Cover illustration by Henry E. Vallely." – Lowery, 1981, p. 84].

82
1937
Weisman, Robert R., 1888-1947 [artist]

Wilson, Buck, 1899- . [pseudonym for Gaylord DuBois, Gaylord][author]

Buck Jones and the two-gun kid / by Gaylord DuBois [pseudonym, Buck Wilson]; illustrated by Robert R. Weisman. – Racine, WI: Whitman Publishing Company (c1937 by Silverbuck, Inc.), c1937. – 425, i.e., [432] p.: b & w ills.; col. ills. on covers & spine; 11.5 x 9 x 4 cm. – (The big little book; 1404)

[Notes: "GW187" – Lowery, 1981. – Hard covers & spine. – "Duane H. Siers" – Stamped on small red-bordered label glued to inside front cover. – "Table of contents" – p. [7]. – Publisher's advertisements. – p. [426-429]. – Library's copy lacks pp. [2-3].

83
1937
Marsh, Norman [artist & author]

Dan Dunn, Secret Operative 48 and the crime master / by Norman Marsh; based on the famous newspaper strip. – Racine, WI: Whitman Publishing Co. (c1937, by Publishers Syndicate, Chicago, Ill.; licensed by Stephen Slesinger, Inc., New York, N.Y.), c1937. — 424, i.e., [432] p.: b & w ills.; col. ills. on covers ; 11.5 x 9.5 x 4 cm. - (The big little book; 1171)

[Notes: "GW177" – Lowery, 1981. – Hard covers & spine. – "Duane H. Siers" – Stamped on inside front cover. – "Table of contents" – p. [7]. – Publisher's advertisements. – pp. [426-429]. – "Crime never pays! Long years in a penitentiary is the only real pay any criminal has ever received for his misdeeds, Dan Dunn." – p. [3].

84
1937
Gould, Chester [author]

Republic Pictures [firm]

Detective Dick Tracy and the Spider Gang / from the movie serial; based on the famous comic strip character; by Chester Gould; retold from the Republic Motion Picture with Ralph Byrd as Dick Tracy, Kay Hughes as Gwen, Smiley Burnette as Mike McGurk, Lee Van Atta as Junior. – Racine, WI: Whitman Publishing Company (c1937 by Chester Gould; licensed by Famous Artists Syndicate, Chicago, Illinois) c1937. – 232, i.e., [240] p.: b & w photos; col. photos on covers & spine; 11.5 x 9 x 4 cm. – (The big little book; 1446)

[Notes: "GW224" – Lowery, 1981. – Hard covers & spine. – "Duane H. Siers" – Stamped on inside front cover. – Publisher's advertisements. – pp. [233-234]. – "Story of the Republic Motion Picture serial"—On front cover. – "Based on the famous newspaper strip" – On spine. – "A scene from the Republic Motion Picture" – On back cover. – Library's copy lacking pp. [5-6].

85 1937
Gould, Chester [artist & author]
Dick Tracy and the hotel murders / By Chester Gould. – Racine, WI: Whitman Publishing Company (c1937, by Chester Gould), c1937 – 424, i.e., [432] p.: b & w ills.; col. ills. on covers & spine; 11.5 x 9 x 4 cm. – (The big little book; 1420)

[Notes: "GW201" – Lowery, 1981. – Hard covers & spine. – "Table of contents" – p. [7]. – Publisher's advertisements. – pp. [426-428]. – "Say Tracy!" Junior exclaimed. "This bell-hop job is risky, all right – see the bullet hole in my cap!" – On back cover].

86 1937
Raymond, Alex, 1909-1956 [artist & author]
Flash Gordon in the water world of Mongo / by Alex Raymond; based on the famous adventure strip. – Racine, WI: Whitman Publishing Company (c1936, 1937, by King Features Syndicate, Inc., New York, N.Y.), c1936, 1937. – 424, i.e., [432] p.: b & w ills.; col. ills. on covers; 11.5 x 9.5 x 4 cm. – (The big little book; 1407)

[Notes: "GW190" – Lowery, 1981. – Hard covers & spine. – "Duane H. Siers" – Stamped on inside front cover. – "Table of contents" – p. [7]. – Publisher's advertisement. – pp. [426-428].

87 1937
Blosser, Merrill [artist & author]
Freckles and the lost diamond mine / by Merrill Blosser; based on the famous NEA comic. – Racine, WI: Whitman Publishing Company, (c1935-36, NEA Services, Inc.; c1937, by Stephen Slesinger Inc., New York, N.Y.), c1937. – [432] p.: b & w ills.; col. ills on covers & spine; 11.5 x 9 x 3 cm. – (The big little book; 1164)

[Notes: "GW173" – Lowery, 1981. – Hard covers & spine. – "Duane H. Siers" – Stamped on inside front cover. – Lacking pp. 423-[432], spine and back cover. – "Based on the famous newspaper strip" – On front cover.]

88 1937
Anderson, Herbert [artist]
Dale, Allen [author]
G-Man and the Radio Bank robberies / by Allen Dale; illustrated by Herbert Anderson. – Racine, WI: Whitman Publishing Company (c1937, by Stephen Slesinger, New York, N.Y.), c1937. – 424, i.e., [432] p.: b & w ills.: col. ills. on covers & spine; 11.5 x 9. x 4 cm.—(The big little book; 1434)

[Copy 1: Notes: "GW215" – Lowery, 1981. – Hard covers & spine. – "Duane H. Siers" – Stamped on inside front cover. – "Table of contents" – p. [7]. – Publisher's advertisements. – pp. [426-428]

[Copy 2: Notes: "GW215" – Lowery, 1981. – Hard covers & spine. – "Table of contents" – p. [7]. – Publisher's advertisements. – pp. [426-428]. – Library's copy 2 lacking spine].

89 1937
[Anderson, Lyman] [artist]
[Arbo, Hal] [artist]
[Wallace, Edgar] [author]
Inspector Wade of Scotland Yard in The mystery of the Red Aces. – Racine, WI: Whitman Publishing Co. (c1937, by King Features Syndicate, Inc., New York, N.Y.), c1937. – 424, i.e., [432] p.: b & w ills.; col. ills. on covers & spine; 11.5 x 9 x 4 cm. – (The big little book 1448)

[Notes: "GW226" – Lowery, 1981. – Hard covers & spine. – "Table of contents" – p. [7]. – Publisher's advertisements. – pp. [426-428]. – "Inspector Wade solves the mystery of the Red Aces." – On front cover. – "Inspector Wade of Scotland Yard: the mystery of the Red Aces." – On spine].

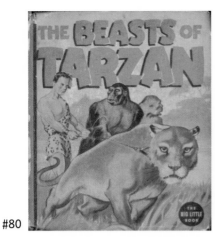

#80

#83

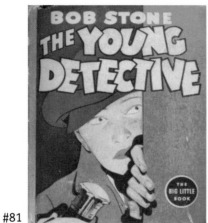

#81

#84

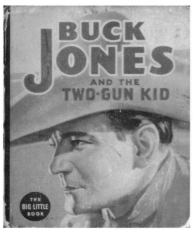

#82

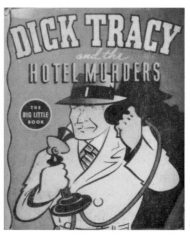

#85

#86

#89

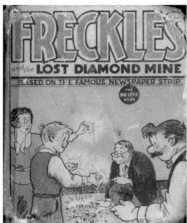

#87

#90

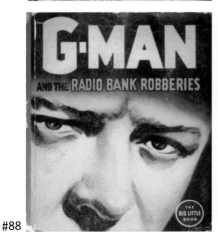

#88

#91

90 1937
Vane, Conrad [author]
Arbo, Hal [cover artist]
International spy: Doctor Doom faces death at dawn / by Conrad Vane. – Racine, WI: Whitman Publishing Co. (c1937 by Stephen Slesinger, Inc., New York, N.Y.), c1937. – 424, i.e., [432] p.: b & w ills.; col. ills. on covers & spine; 11.5 x 9.5 x 4 cm. – (The big little book; 1148)

[Notes: "GW168" – Lowery, 1981. – Hard covers & spine. – "Duane H. Siers" – Stamped on inside front cover. – "Table of contents" – p. [7]. – Publisher's advertisements. – pp. [426-429]. – "Arbo" – Signature on front cover].

91 1937
Vallely, Henry R. [artist]
Daniels, Leslie N. [author]
Jack Armstrong, the all-American boy and the ivory treasure / by Leslie N. Daniels, Jr.; illustrated by Henry E. Vallely. – Racine, WI: Whitman Publishing Co. (c1937, by General Mills, Inc.), c1937. – 424, i.e., [432] p.: b & w ills.; col. ills. on covers & spine; 11.5 x 9 x 4 cm. – (The big little book; 1435)

[Notes: "GW216" – Lowery, 1981. – Hard covers & spine. – "Duane H. Siers" – Stamped on inside front cover. – "Table of contents" – p. [7]. – Publisher's advertisements. – pp. [426-427]. – "Jack Armstrong and the ivory treasure"; "Based on the famous radio series." – On front cover].

92 1937
Vallely, Henry E. [artist]
Massey, Morrell [author]
Junior G-Men and the counterfeiters / by Morrell Massey; illustrated by Henry E. Vallely. – Racine, WI: Whitman Publishing Co., c1937. – 424, i.e., [432] p.: b & w ills.; col. ills. on covers & spine; 11.5 x 9 x 4 cm. – (The big little book; 1442)

[Notes: "GW221" – Lowery, 1981. – Hard covers & spine. – "Duane H. Siers" – Stamped on inside front cover. – "Table of contents" – p. [7]. – Publisher's advertisements. – pp. [426-429]].

93 1937
Carter, Ad, 1895-1957 [artist & author]
Just kids / by Ad Carter; based on the famous comic strip. – Racine, WI: Whitman Publishing Company (c1937, by King Features Syndicate, Inc., New York, N.Y.), c1937. – 424, i.e., [432] p.: b & w ills.; col. ills. on covers; 11.5 x 9 x 4 cm. – (The big little book; 1401)

[Notes: "GW184" – Lowery, 1981. – Hard covers & spine. – "Duane H. Siers" – Stamped on inside front cover. – "Table of contents" – p. [7]. – Publisher's advertisements. – pp. [436-428]. – "Based on the famous comic strip" – On spine. – "Hey, look! That's Genevieve, — my new pet!" – On back cover].

94 1937
Mueller, Charles [artists]
Ray, Irene, 1903-   . [pseudonym for Margaret Sutton] [author]
Kay Darcy and the mystery hideout / by Irene Ray; illustrated by Charles Mueller; a Kay Darcy detective story. – Racine, WI: Whitman Publishing Co., c1937. – 292, i.e., [300] p.: b & w ills.; col. ills. on covers & spine; 11.5 x 9 x 4 cm. – (The big little book; 1411)

[Notes: "GW194" – Lowery, 1981. – Hard covers & spine. – "Duane H. Siers" – Stamped on inside front cover. – Publisher's advertisements. – pp. [294-298?]. – Library's copy lacking, pp. [295-298]. – "Irene Ray was the pen name for Margaret Sutton..." – Lowery, 1981, p. 80].

95 1937
Andersen, Alice [artist & author]
Mary Lee and the mystery of the Indian beads / by Alice Andersen. - Racine, WI: Whitman Publishing Company, c1937. - 292, i.e., [300] p.: b & w ills.; col. ills. on covers & spine; 11.5 x 9 x 4 cm. - (The big little book; 1438)

[Notes: "GW218" - Lowery, 1981. - Hard covers & spine. - Publisher's advertisements. - pp. [294-297].

96 1937
Disney, Walt, 1901-1966 [artist & author]
[Gottfredson, Floyd] [artist & author]
Walt Disney Enterprises [firm]
Mickey Mouse runs his own newspaper / by Walt Disney. - Racine, WI: Whitman Publishing Company (c1937, by Walt Disney Enterprises, Hollywood, Calif.), c1937. - 292, i.e., [300] p.: b & w ills.; col. ills. on covers & spine; 11.5 x 9 x 4 cm. - (The big little book; 1409)

[Notes: "GW192" - Lowery, 1981. - Hard covers & spine. - "Duane H. Siers" - Stamped on inside front cover. - "Table of contents" - p. [7]. - Publisher's advertisements. - pp. [294-297]. - "Her she comes Mickey!" - On back cover. - "From comic strip story: March 2, 1935 to May 30, 1935." - Lowery, 1981, p. 79].

97 1937
Lantz, Walter [author]
[Packer, Eleanor Lewis?] [author]
[Universal Pictures?] [firm]
[Oswald Rabbit plays G man / by Walter Lantz. - Racine, WI: Whitman Publishing Company, c1937]. - [240] p.: b & w ills.[adapted from motion picture animation]; col. ills. on covers; 11.5 x 9 x 4 cm. - (The big little book; 1403)

[Notes: "GW186" - Lowery, 1981. - Hard covers & spine. - "Duane H. Siers" - Stamped on

inside front cover. - Library's copy lacking pp. [3-4, 234-237].

98 1937
Lee, Dougal [artist & author]
Pat Nelson, ace of test pilots / written and illustrated by Dougal Lee. - Racine, WI: Whitman Publishing Company, c1937. - 424, i.e., [43] p.: b & w ills.; col. ills. on covers & spine; 11.5 x 9 x 4 cm. - (The big little book; 1445)

[Notes: "GW223" - Lowery, 1981. - Hard covers & spine. - Publisher's advertisements. - pp. [295-297].

99 1937
Vallely, Henry E. [artist]
Heisenfelt, Kathryn [author]
Peggy Brown and the runaway auto trailer / by Kathryn Heisenfelt; illustrated by Henry E. Vallely. - Racine, WI: Whitman Publishing Company, c1937. - 294, i.e., [300] p.: b & w ills.; col. ills. on covers & spine; 11.5 x 9 x 4 cm. - (The big little book; 1427)

[Notes: "GW208" - Lowery, 1981. - Hard covers & spine. - "Duane H. Siers" - Stamped on inside front cover. - Publisher's advertisements. - pp. [295-297].

100 1937
Segar, E.C. , 1894-1938
(Elzie Crisler) [artist & author]
[Popeye in quest of his poopdeck pappy / by E.C. Segar. - Racine, WI: Whitman Publishing Company, c1937]. - 424, i.e., [432] p.: b & w ills.; col. ills. on covers & spine; 11.5 x 9 x 4 cm. - (The big little book; 1450)

[Notes: "GW228" - Lowery, 1981. - Hard covers & spine. - "Duane H. Siers" - Stamped on inside front cover. - Publisher's advertisements. - pp. [426-428]. - Library's copy lacking pp. [3-24].

#92

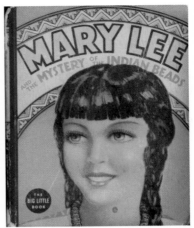

#95

#93

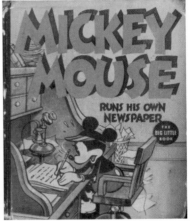

#96

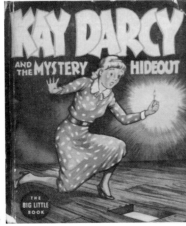

#94

#97

101 1937
Sullivan, Eddie [artist]
Schmidt, Charlie [author]
Radio patrol: the radio police sleuths trail the safeblowers / by Eddie Sullivan and Charlie Schmidt; based on the famous newspaper strip. – Racine, WI: Whitman Publishing Co. (c1937 by King Features Syndicate, Inc., Great Britain...), c1937. – 424, i.e., [432] p.: b & w ills.; col. ills. on covers & spine: 11.5 x 9 x 4 cm. – (The big little book; 1173)

[Notes: "GW179" – Lowery, 1981. – Hard covers & spine. – "Duane H. Siers" – Stamped on inside front cover. – "Table of contents", p. [7] – Publisher's advertisements. – pp. [426-429] – "Radio patrol: trailing the safeblowers"; "Based on the famous newspaper strip" – On cover & spine].

102 1937
Young, William Mark [artist]
Beach, Rex, 1877-1949 [author]
Rex Beach's Jaragu of the jungle: adventures among the Indians of Central America / illustrated by Wm. Mark Young. – Racine, WI: Whitman Publishing Co. (c1937, by Stephen Slesinger, Inc., New York, N.Y.), c1937. – [432] p.: b & w ills.; col. ills. on covers; 11.5 x 9 x 4 cm. – (The big little book; 1424)

[Notes: "GW205" – Lowery, 1981. – Hard covers & spine. – "Table of contents", p. [7]. – Library's copy lacking pp. [3-4, 423-429]. – "Jaragu, the jungle boy, received the surprise of his life when a gigantic bird making a loud whirring noise came down to the beach in Central America and was still, as though it had been killed – but what looked like a man climbed out of its remains!" – On back cover].

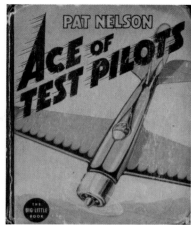

#98

#99

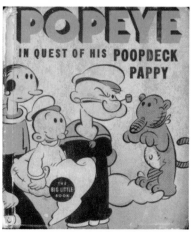

#100

103
1937
Saxton, Steve [author]

Riders of the lone trails / by Steve Saxton. – Racine, WI: Whitman Publishing Co. (c1937, by Stephen Slesinger, Redding Ridge, Conn.), c1937. – [300] p.: b & w ills.; col. ills. on covers & spine; 11.5 x 9 x 4 cm. – (The big little book; 1425)

[Notes: "GW206" – Lowery, 1981. – Hard covers & spine. – "Duane H. Siers" – Stamped on p.[3]. – "Table of contents", p. [7]. – Library's copy lacking pp. [279-298].

104
1937
[Disney, Walt, 1901-1966] [author]
[Taliaferro, Al, 1905-1969] [artist & author]

[Silly symphony featuring Donald Duck / Walt Disney. – Racine, WI: Whitman Publishing Company, 1937]. – [432] p.: b & w ills.; col. ills. on covers and spine; 11.5 x 9 . 4 cm. – (The big little book; 1169)

[Notes: "GW176" – Lowery, 1981. – Hard covers & spine. – "Duane H. Siers" – Stamped on small red-bordered label glued to inside front cover. – Library's copy lacks pp. [3 (title page)-28, 425-428, & spine].

105
1937
Disney, Walt, 1901-1966 [author]
[Taliaferro, Al, 1905-1969] [artist & author]
Walt Disney Enterprises [firm]

Silly symphony featuring Donald Duck and his (mis)adventures / by Walt Disney. – Racine, WI: Whitman Publishing Company (c 1937, by Walt Disney Enterprises, Hollywood, Calif), 1937. – 424, i.e., [432] p.: b & w ills.; col. ills. on covers and spine; 11.5 x 9 . 4 cm. – (The big little book; 1441)

[Notes: "GW220" – Lowery, 1981. – Hard covers & spine. – "Table of contents" – p [7]. – Publisher's advertisements. – pp. [426-429].

106
1937
Youngren, Milt [artist]
Saxton, Steve [author]

The Texas Kid / by Steve Saxton; illustrated by Milt Youngren. – Racine, WI: Whitman Publishing Co. (c1937 by Stephen Slesinger, Redding Ridge, Conn.), c1937. – 424, i.e., [432] p.: b & w ills.; col. ills. on covers; 11.5 x 9 x 4 cm. – (The big little book; 1429)

[Notes: "GW210" – Lowery, 1981. – Hard covers & spine. – "Duane H. Siers" – Stamped on inside front cover. – "Table of contents" – p. [7]. – Publisher's advertisements. – pp. [426-429].

107
1937
Vallely, Henry E. [artist]
West, Wilton [author]

Tom Mix and the hoard of Montezuma / by Wilton West; illustrated by Henry E. Vallely. – Racine, WI: Whitman Publishing Company (c1937, by Stephen Slesinger, Inc., New York, N.Y.), c1937. – 424, i.e., [432] p.: b & w ills.; col. ills. on covers & spine; 11.5 x 9 x 4 cm. – (The big little book; 1462)

[Notes: "GW240" – Lowery, 1981. – Hard covers & spine. – "Duane H. Siers" – Stamped on inside front cover. – "Table of contents" – p. [7]. – Publisher's advertisements. – pp. [426-428].

108
1937
Arbo, Hal [artist]
Wilson, Buck, 1899- . [pseudonym for Gaylord DuBois] [author]

Tom Mix in the range war / by Buck Wilson [pseudonym for Gaylord DuBois]; illustrations by Hal Arbo. – Racine, WI: Whitman Publishing Co. (c 1937 by

Stephen Slesinger, Inc.), c1937. – 424, i.e., [432] p.: b & w ills.; col. ills. on covers & spine; 11.5 x 9 x 4 cm. – (The big little book; 1166)

[Notes: "GW175" – Lowery, 1981. – Hard covers & spine. – "Duane H. Siers" – Stamped on inside front cover. – "Table of contents" – p. [7-8]. – Publisher's advertisements. – pp. [425-428].

109 1937
Grey, Zane, 1875-1939 [author]
Arbo, Hal [cover artist]
Zane Grey's Tex Thorne comes out of the West. – Racine, WI: Whitman Publishing Company (c1936, 1937 by Stephen Slesinger, Inc., and King Features Syndicate, Inc.; c1937 by Stephen Slesinger, Inc., New York, N.Y.), c1937. – 424, i.e., [432] p.: b & w ills.; col. ills. on covers & spine; 11.5 x 9 x 4 cm. – (The big little book; 1440)

[Notes: "GW219" – Lowery, 1981. – Hard covers & spine. – "Table of contents" – p. [7]. – Publisher's advertisements. – pp. [426-428]. – "Based on the famous comic strip" – On front cover and spine. – Cover illustrations signed "Arbo"].

110 1938
Miller, Frank [artist & author]
Barney Baxter in the air with the Eagle Squadron / by Frank Miller. – Racine, WI: Whitman Publishing Company (c1936, 1937, 1938 by King Features Syndicate, Inc., New York, New York), c1938. – 424, i.e., [432] p.: b & w ills.; col. ills. on covers & spine; 11.5 x 9 x 4 cm. – (The big little book; 1459)

[Notes: "GW237" – Lowery, 1981. – Hard covers & spine. – "Duane H. Siers" – Stamped on inside front cover. – "Table of contents" – p. [7]. – Publisher's advertisements. – pp. [426-428]. – "Based on the famous comic strip" – On front cover].

111 1938
Weisman, Robert R. [artist]
Wilson, Buck, 1899- . [pseudonym for Gaylord DuBois] [author]
Blaze Brandon with the Foreign Legion / by Gaylord Du Bois [Buck Wilson, pseudonym]; illustrated by Robert R. Weisman. – Racine, WI: Whitman Publishing Company, c1938. – 424, i.e., [432] p.: b & w ills.; col. ills. on covers & spine; 11.5 x 9 x 4 cm. – (The big little book; 1447)

[Notes: "GW225" – Lowery, 1981. – Hard covers & spine. – "Table of contents" – p. [7-8]. – Publisher's advertisements. – pp. [426-429].

112 1938
Myers, Irwin [artist]
The Hawk's Trail [radio program]
Captain Frank Hawks, famous air ace, and the League of Twelve / based on the famous radio series "The Hawk's Trail"; illustrated by Irwin Myers. – Racine, WI: Whitman Publishing Company (c1938, by Stephen Slesinger, Inc., New York, N.Y.), c1938. – 424, i.e., [432] p.: b & w ills.; col. ills. on covers & spine; 11.5 x 9 x 4 cm. – (The big little book; 1444)

[Notes: "GW222" – Lowery, 1981. – Hard covers & spine. – "Duane H. Siers" – Stamped on small red-bordered label glued to inside front cover. – "Table of contents" – p. [7]. – Publisher's advertisements, pp. [426-429]. – "Captain Frank Hawks, air ace, and the League of Twelve." – On front cover and spine. – "Based on the famous radio adventure series." – On spine. – Library's copy lacking pp. [3-4].

#101

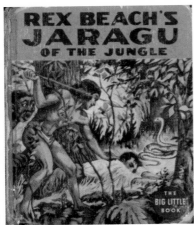

#102

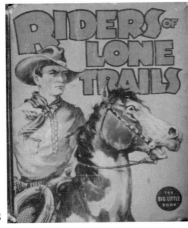

#103

#104

#105

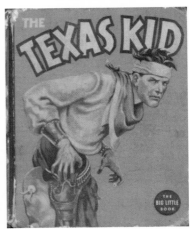

#106

#107

#110

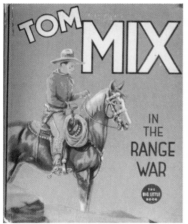

#108

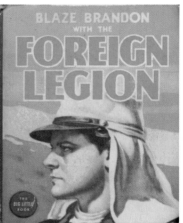

#111

#109

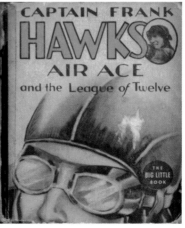

#112

113 1938
Kress, Joseph R. [artist]
McClusky, Thorp [author]
[Chuck Malloy, railroad detective on the Streamliner / by Thorp McClusky. – Racine, WI: Whitman Publishing Company, c1938]. – 282, i.e., [300] p.: b & w ills.; col. ills. on covers; 11.5 x 9 x 5 cm. – (The big little book; 1453)

[Notes: "GW231" – Lowery, 1981. – Hard covers & spine. – "Duane H. Siers" – Stamped on inside front cover. – "Table of contents" – p. [7]. – Publisher's advertisements. – pp. [29?-297]. – Library's copy lacking pp. [2-3 (title page),283-296] & spine].

114 1938
Williamson, R.M. [artist]
Coach Bernie Bierman's Brick Barton and the winning eleven / illustrated by R. M. Williamson. – Racine, WI: Whitman Publishing Company, c1938. – 292, i.e., [300] p.: b & w ills.; col. ills. on covers & spine; 11.5 x 9 x 4 cm. – ([The big little book]; 1480)

[Notes: "GW251b" – Lowery, 1981. – Hard covers & spine. – "Duane H. Siers" – Stamped on inside front cover. – "Table of contents" – p. [7]. – Publisher's advertisements. – pp. [294-296]. – "Note: Except the name of Coach Bernie Bierman, used here by special arrangement, the names and events in this story are entirely fictitious." – Verso of title page. – "Logo on cover has been overprinted.– Lowery, 1981, p. 92].

115 1938
Harman, Fred
[artist & author]
Arbo, Hal [artist]
Cowboy lingo: boy's book of Western facts / written and illustrated by Fred Harman, creator of "Bronc Peeler". – Racine, WI: Whitman Publishing Company (c1938, by Stephen Slesinger, Inc., New York, N.Y.), c1938. –292, i.e., [300] p.: b & w ills.; col. ills. on covers; 11.5 x 9.5 x 3 cm. – (The big little book; 1457)

[Notes: "GW235" – Lowery, 1981. – Hard covers & spine. – "Duane H. Siers" – Stamped on inside front cover. – "Table of contents" – p. [6-9]. – Library's copy lacking pp. [53-78, 239-260, 263-264, 293-296] – Cover illustrations signed: "Arbo"].

116 1938
Packer, Eleanor Lewis
[author]
McConville, Bernard [author]
Drake, Oliver [author]
Autry, Gene, 1907- . [actor]
Republic Pictures [firm]
Gene Autry in Public cowboy No. 1 / retold by Eleanor Packer from the Republic Motion Picture starring Gene Autry, with Smiley Burnette, Ann Rutherford, William Farnum; associate producer, Sol. C. Siegel; directed by Joseph Kane; screen play by Oliver Drake; original story by Bernard McConville. – Racine, WI: Whitman Publishing Company, c1938. – 236, i.e., [240] p.: b & w photos; col. photos on covers; 11.5 x 9 x 4 cm. – (The big little book; 1433)

[Notes: "GW214" – Lowery, 1981. – Hard covers & spine. – Publisher's advertisements. – pp. [238]. "Republic Pictures presents: Gene Autry in Public cowboy No. 1" – On front cover].

117 1938
Winter, R.B. [artist & author]
Hal Hardy in the Lost Valley of the Giants: the world 1,000,000 years ago / by R.B. Winter. – Racine, WI: Whitman Publishing Company, c1938. – 292, i.e., [300] p.: b & w ills.; col. ills. on covers & spine; 11.5 x 9 x 4 cm. – (The big little book; 1413)

[Notes: "GW196" – Lowery, 1981. – Hard covers & spine. – Publisher's advertisements. – pp. [294-297]. – "Hal Hardy in the Lost Land of Giants: the world 1,000,000 years ago." – On cover & spine].

118 1938
Anderson, Herbert [artist]
Saxton, Steve [author]
Jim Craig, State Trooper, and the kidnapped governor / by Steve Saxton; illustrated by Herbert Anderson. – Racine, WI: Whitman Publishing Company (c1938, by Stephen Slesinger, New York, N.Y.), c1938. – 424, i.e., [432] p.: b & w ills.; col. ills. on covers & spine; 11.5 x 9 x 4 cm. – (The big little book; 1466)

[Notes: "GW242" – Lowery, 1981. – Hard covers & spine. – "Duane H. Siers" – Stamped on inside front cover. – "Table of contents" – p. [7]. – Publisher's advertisements. – pp. [426-427].

119 1938
Hess, Sol, 1872-1941
[author]
Junior Nebb on the Diamond-Bar Ranch / by Sol Hess; based on the famous newspaper strip "The Nebbs". – Racine, WI: Whitman Publishing Company (c1938, by Sol Hess), c1938. – 288, i.e., [300] p.: b & w ills.; col. ills. on covers; 11.5 x 9 x 4 cm. –([The big little book; 1422])

[Notes: "GW203b" – Lowery, 1981. – Hard covers & spine. – "Duane H. Siers" – Stamped on small red-bordered label glued to inside front cover. – "Table of contents" – p. [5]. – Library's copy lacks spine, back cover and pp. [290-300]. – "Logo on cover has been overprinted" – Lowery, 1981, p. 82].

120 1938
Myer, Irwin [artist]
Loomis, Rex [author]
Ken Maynard in Western Justice / by Rex Loomis; illustrated by Irwin Myers. – Racine, WI: Whitman Publishing Co. (c1938, by Ken Maynard), c1938. – 424, i.e., [432] p.: b & w ills.; col. ills. on covers & spine; 11.5 x 9 x 4 cm. – (The big little book; 1430)

[Notes: "GW211" – Lowery, 1981. – Hard covers & spine. – "Duane H. Siers" – Stamped on inside front cover. – Publisher's advertisements. – pp. [426-429].

121 1938
McClure, Darrell, 1903-1987
[artist]
Walsh, Brandon [author]
Little Annie Rooney on the highway to adventure / by Brandon Walsh; based on the famous newspaper strip. – Racine, WI: Whitman Publishing Company (c1936, 1937, 1938, by King Features Syndicate, Inc., New York, N.Y.), c1936, 1937, 1938. – 424, i.e., [432] p.: b & w ills.; col. ills. on covers & spine; 11.5 x 9 x 4 cm. – (The big little book; 1406)

[Notes: "GW189" – Lowery, 1981. – Hard covers & spine. – "Duane H. Siers" – Stamped on inside front cover. – "Table of contents" – p. [7]. – Publisher's advertisements. – pp. [426-428]. – Front cover illustration signed: "Darrell McClure" – "Based on the famous newspaper strip" – On back cover].

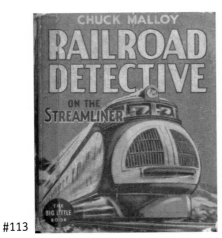

#113

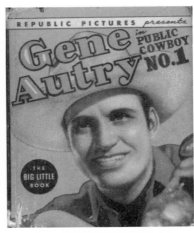

#116

#114

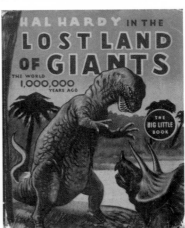

#117

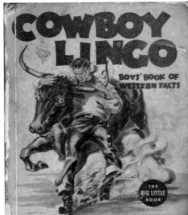

#115

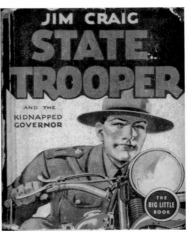

#118

#119

#122

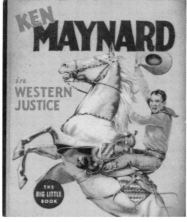

#120

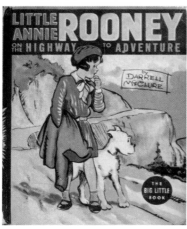

#121

122 1938
Gray, Harold [artist & author]
Little Orphan Annie and the mysterious shoemaker / by Harold Gray; based on the famous newspaper strip. – Racine, WI: Whitman Publishing Co. (c1938, by Harold Gray, Colton-on-Hudson, N.Y.), c1938. – 424, i.e., [432] p.: b & w ills.; col. ills. on covers & spine; 11.5 x 9 x 3.5 cm. – (The big little book; 1449)

[Notes: "GW227" – Lowery, 1981. – Hard covers & spine. – "Duane H. Siers" – Stamped on inside front cover. – "Table of contents" – p. [7]. – Publisher's advertisements. – pp. [426-42?]. – Library's copy lacking pp. [3-4, 426-430]. – "Little Orphan Annie and her dog Sandy watched the mysterious stranger as he walked along on his unknown errand" – On back cover].

123 1938
Weisman, Robert R. [artist]
Wilson, Buck, 1899-   . [pseudonym for Gaylord Du Bois] [author]
Striker, Fran, 1903-1962 [author]
The Lone Ranger and the menace of Murder Valley (with Silver and Tonto): a story / by Buck Wilson [pseudonym];

illustrated by Robert R. Weisman; based on the famous radio series by Fran Striker. – Racine, WI: Whitman Publishing Company (c1938, by The Lone Ranger, Inc.; licensed by Famous Artists Syndicate, Chicago, Ill), c1938. – 424, i.e., [432] p.: b & w ills.; col. ills. on covers & spine; 11.5 x 9 x 4 cm. – (The big little book; 1465)

[Notes: "GW241" – Lowery, 1981. – Hard covers & spine. – "Duane H. Siers" – Stamped on inside front cover. – "Table of contents" – p. [7]. – Publisher's advertisements. – pp. [426-428].

124
1938
Packer, Eleanor Lewis [author]

Paramount Pictures, Inc. [firm]

Paramount Pictures present: Wells Fargo: a story of exciting days of the Old West / featuring Joel McCrea, Bob Burns and Frances Dee; a Frank Lloyd Production; retold by Eleanor Packer: the cast also includes Lloyd Nolan, Ralph Morgan, Henry O'Neill, Mary Nash, Porter Hall, John Mack Brown, Robert Cummings, Barlowe Borland. – Racine, WI: Whitman Publishing Company, c1938. – 236, i.e., [240] p.: b & w photo; col. photos on covers & spine; 11.5 x 9 x 4 cm. – (The big little book; 1471)

[Notes: "GW246" – Lowery, 1981. – Hard covers & spine. – "Duane H. Siers" – Stamped on inside front cover. – p. [7]. – "Wells Fargo. A Paramount Picture featuring Joel McCrea, Bob Burns, Frances Dee. A Frank Lloyd Production. Read the book, see the picture." – On front cover. – "Wells Fargo: a story of the exciting days of the Old West" – On spine].

125
1938
Mosley, Zack [artist & author]

Smilin' Jack and his stratosphere plane / by Zack Mosley; based on the famous adventure strip. – [Ice cream cone premium edition]. – Racine, WI: Whitman Publishing Co. (c1937, 1938 by Zack Mosley; licensed by Famous Artists Syndicate, Chicago, Ill.), c1937, 1938. – 126, i.e., [128] p.; b & w ills.; col. ill. on front cover; 9 x 9 x 1 cm. – ([The big little book]; Buddy book; #2)

[Notes: "GWp63" – Lowery, 1981. – Soft covers. – Staple bound. – "Duane H. Siers" – Stamped twice on inside front cover. – Library's copy lacks coupon on p. [127?]. – "You have received this BUDDY BOOK by saving 12 BUDDY BOOK coupons. You can get many other thrilling BUDDY BOOKS like this one. You cannot buy them! You cannot get them in any other way except by saving BUDDY BOOK coupons. Every time you buy an ICE CREAM CONE be sure to ask for a BUDDY BOOK coupon! Enjoy a Double Treat! Your favorite ice cream in a delicious cake cone – and BRAND NEW BOOKS about your favorite heroes FREE! Free! GREAT BIG BOOKS Free! At the back of each BUDDY BOOK you will find a BIG BOOK coupon. Save 12 of these and get a GREAT BIG BOOK – hard bound – hundreds of exciting pages – beautifully illustrated – books you have always wanted! When you have the 12 BIG BOOK coupons take them in to your dealer and get YOUR GREAT BIG BOOK ABSOLUTELY FREE. Ask your folks and friends to save BUDDY BOOK coupons for you. THIS BOOK IS NOT TO BE SOLD. No.2."– On back cover].

["A third set of 12 books was produced in 1938 at the end of the Golden Age. These were labeled <u>Buddy Books</u> and obtained by purchasing ice cream cones and saving the "Buddy Book Coupons" given with each purchase. Twelve coupons could be turned in for one premium book. The Buddy Books were identical to the previous books in size (3½ x 3½) and format, however, each was 128 pages long, and the book's coupon was printed on the last page rather than on the back cover." – Lowery, 1981, p. 97-98].

126 1938
Berndt, 1899-1980 [author]
Smitty in Going native / by Walter Berndt; based on the famous comic strip. – Racine, WI: Whitman Publishing Company (c1938, by Walter Berndt), c1938. – 292, i.e., [300] p.: b & w ills.; col. ills. on covers & spine; 11.5 x 9 x 3 cm. – (The big little book; 1477)

[Notes: "GW249b" – Lowery, 1981. – Hard covers & spine. – "Duane H. Siers" – Stamped on inside front cover. – Library copy lacking pp. [293-298]. – "Based on the famous comic strip" – On front cover. – "Logo on cover has been overprinted" – Lowery, 1981, p. 91].

127 1938
Holman, Bill, 1903- .
[artist & author]
Smokey Stover, the foo fighter / by Bill Holman; based on the famous comic strip. – Racine, WI: Whitman Publishing Company, c1938. – 424, i.e., [432] p.: b & w ills.; col. ills. on covers; 11.5 x 9 x 4 cm. – ([The big little book; 1421])

[Notes: "GW202" – Lowery, 1981. – Hard covers & spine. – "Duane H. Siers" – Stamped on inside front cover. – "Table of contents" – p. [7]. – Library's copy lacks spine, back cover & pp. [425-432].

128 1938
Vallely, Henry E. [artist]
Packer, Eleanor Lewis [author]
Bergen, Edgar, 1903-1978 [ventriloquist]
The story of Charlie McCarthy from the Edgar Bergen-Charlie McCarthy radio programs / retold by Eleanor Packer. – Racine, WI: Whitman Publishing Company (c1938, by McCarthy, Inc.), c1938. – 280, i.e., [288] p.: b & w ills.:

col. ills. on covers & spine; 11.5 x 9.5 x 3 cm. – (The big little book; 1456)

[Notes: "GW234" – Lowery, 1981. – Hard covers & spine. – "Duane H. Siers" – Stamped on inside front cover. – "Table of contents" – p. [5]. – Publisher's advertisements. – pp. [282-284].

129 1938
Walt Disney Enterprises
[firm]
The story of Walt Disney's Snow White and the Seven Dwarfs / by the Staff of the Walt Disney Studios; based on the Walt Disney motion picture. – Authorized edition. – Racine, WI: Whitman Publishing Company (c1938, by Walt Disney Enterprises, Hollywood, Calif.), c1938. – 280, i.e., [288] p.: b & w ills.; col. ills. on covers & spine; 11.5 x 9 x 4 cm. – (The big little book; 1460)

[Notes: "GW238" – Lowery, 1981. – Hard covers & spine. – "Table of contents" – p. [5]. – Publisher's advertisements. – pp. [282-284]. – "Walt Disney's Snow White and the Seven Dwarfs" – On cover. – Library's copy has many hand illustrations hand colored with crayons].

130 1938
Forrest, Hal [artist & author]
Tailspin Tommy and the sky bandits / by Hal Forrest; based on the famous adventure strip. – Racine, WI: Whitman Publishing Company (c1938, by Stephen Slesinger, Inc., New York, N.Y.), c1938. – 424, i.e., [432] p.: b & w ills.; col. ills. on covers & spine; 11.5 x 9 x 4 cm. – (The big little book; 1494)

[Notes: "GW254a" – Lowery, 1981. – Hard covers & spine. – "Duane H. Siers" – Stamped on inside front cover. – "Table of contents" – p. [7]. – Publisher's advertisements. – pp. [426-428]. – "Based on the famous adventure ship" – On front cover].

#123

#126

#124

#127

#125

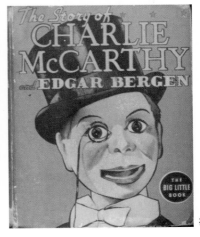

#128

131 1938

Burroughs, Edgar Rice, 1875-1950 [author]
Principal Pictures, Inc. [firm]
Twentieth Century-Fox [firm]
Tarzan's revenge: a story / based on the motion picture featuring Glen Morris and Eleanor Holm; produced by Principal Pictures, Inc.; distributed by Twentieth Century-Fox; a "Tarzan of the Apes" adventure by Edgar Rice Burroughs. – Racine, WI: Whitman Publishing Company (c1938, by Edgar Rice Burroughs, Tarzana, Calif.), c1938. – 424, i.e., [432] p.: b & w ills.; col. ills. on covers & spine; 11.5 x 9 x 4 cm. – ([The big little book]; 1488)

[Notes: "GW252b" – Lowery, 1981. – Hard covers & spine. – "Duane H. Siers" – Stamped on inside front cover. – "Table of contents" – p. [7]. – Publisher's advertisements. – pp. [426-428]. – 'Logo on cover has been over-printed" – Lowery, 1981, p. 93].

132 1938

Caniff, Milton Arthur, 1907-   . [artist & author]
Terry and the pirates shipwrecked on a desert island / by Milton Caniff. – Racine, WI: Whitman Publishing Co., c1938. – 424, i.e., [432] p.: b & w ills.; col. ills. on covers & spine; 11.5 x 9 x 4 cm. – (The big little book; 1412)

[Notes: "GW195" – Lowery, 1981. – Hard covers & spine. – "Duane H. Siers" – Stamped on inside front cover. – "Table of contents" – p. [7]. – Publisher's advertisements. – pp. [426-428]. – "Based on the famous comic strip Terry and the pirates" – On spine].

133 1938

Disney, Walt, 1901-1966 [author]
Walt Disney Enterprises [firm]
Walt Disney's Pluto the pup / by Walt Disney. – Racine, WI: Whitman Publishing Company (c1938, by Walt Disney Enterprises, Hollywood, Calif.), c1938. – 424, i.e., [432] p.: b & w ills.; col. ills. on covers & spine; 11.5 x 9 x 4 cm. – (The big little book; 1467)

[Notes: "GW243" – Lowery, 1981. – Hard covers & spine. – "Table of contents" – p. [5]. – Publisher's advertisements. – pp. [426-429].

134 1938

Crane, Roy [artist & author]
Wash Tubbs and Captain Easy hunting for whales / by Roy Crane; based on the NEA comic strip. – Racine, WI: Whitman Publishing Co. (c1933, by NEA Service, Inc.; c1938, by Stephen Slesinger, Inc., New York, N.Y.), c1938. – 424, i.e., [432] p.: b & w ills.; col. ills. on covers & spine; 11.5 x 9 x 4 cm. – (The big little book; 1455)

[Notes: "GW233" – Lowery, 1981. – Hard covers & spine. – "Duane H. Siers" – Stamped on inside front cover. – "Table of contents" – p. [7]. – Publisher's advertisements. – pp. [426-428]. – "Based on the famous adventure strip" – On back over].

#129

#132

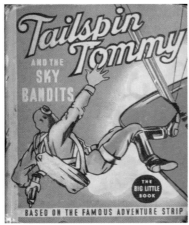

#130

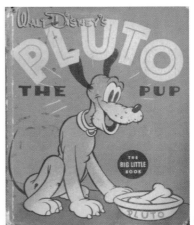

#133

#131

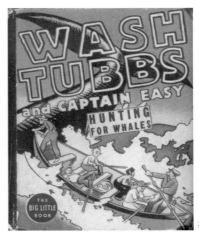

#134

58

#135

#136

135 ¹⁹³⁸
Segar, E.C., 1894-1938
(Elzie Crisler) [artist & author]

Wimpy, the hamburger eater / by Segar; based on the famous comic strip "Thimble Theatre Starring Popeye". – Racine, WI: Whitman Publishing Company (1919, 1929, 1933, 1936 & 1938 by King Features Syndicate, Inc., New York, N.Y.), c1938. – 424, i.e., [432] p.: b & w ills.; col. ills. on covers & spine; 11.5 x 9 x 4 cm. – (The big little book; 1458)

[Notes: "GW236" – Lowery, 1981. – Hard covers & spine. – "Duane H. Siers" – Stamped on inside front cover. – "Table of contents" – p. [7]. – Publisher's advertisements. – pp. [426-428].

136 ¹⁹³⁸
Grey, Zane, 1872-1939
[author]

Zane Grey's King of the Royal Mounted gets his man. / Based on the famous adventure strip. – Racine, WI: Whitman Publishing Co. (c1936, by Stephen Slesinger, Inc., and King Features Syndicate, Inc.; c1938, by Stephen Slesinger, Inc., New York, N.Y.), c1938. – 424, i.e., [432] p.: b & w ills.; col. ills. on covers & spine; 11.5 x 9 x 4 cm. – (The big little book; 1452)

[Notes: "GW230" – Lowery, 1981. – Hard covers & spine. – "Duane H. Siers" – Stamped on inside front cover. – "Table of contents" – p. [7]. – Publisher's advertisements. – pp. [426-428]. – "Based on the famous newspaper strip" – On back cover].

Selected Bibliography and Websites

BIBLIOGRAPHY

Big Little Times, v. 1, #1 (1982)-   . – Danville, CA: Big Little Book Club, 1982-   . Monthly newsletter.

Big Little Times: 10-year anniversary issue, 1982-1992. – Danville, CA: Big Little Book Collector's Club of America, 1991. – 51 p.

Big Little Times 20-year Index, 1982-2001. – Danville, CA: Big Little Book Club, 2002. – 39 p.

Borden, Bill with Steven Posner. – The big book of Big little books. San Francisco, CA: Chronicle Books, 1997. – 119 p.

Cohen, Hal L. – Official guide to comic books and Big little books…: the price to buy & sell. – Florence, AL: House of Collectibles, 1974. – 264 p.

Complete listing of BLBs and related items. – Danville, CA: Big Little Book Club, 1997. – 76 p.

A guide to Dick Tracy Big Little Books. – Danville, CA: Big Little Book Club, 1995. – 48 p.

A guide to the Tarzan Big Little Books. – Danville, CA: Big Little Book Club, 1996. – 188 p.

How BLBs were made. – IN: **Big Little Times 20-year Index, 1982-2001**. – Danville, CA: Big Little Book Club, 2002. pp. 33-39.

Jacobs, Larry. – Big little books: a collector's reference & value guide. Paducah, NY: Collector Books, 1996. – 175 p.

Jewish Journal. – Deerfield couple donate Big Little Books / by Steven Sands. – [Boca Raton, FL?]:, p. 25B+ (Oct. 23, 1986)

L-W Book Sales (Firm). – Price guide to Big little books & Better little, Jumbo, Tiny tales, A fast-action story, etc. – Gas City, IN: L-W Book Sales, 1995. – 104 p.

Lowery, Lawrence F. – Lowery's The collector's guide to Big Little Books and similar books.– Danville, CA: Educational Research and Applications Corporation, 1981. – 378 p.

MacDonald, Roderick. – A study of the Big-Little Book. – Minneapolis, MN: University of Minnesota, 1959. – 14 leaves. (Thesis, M.A.)

Miami Herald. – The rare essentials [Bienes Center opens] / by Elisa Turner. – Miami, FL:, p 1I + 7 (Jan. 12, 1997)

Michigan State University, Russel B. Nye Popular Cultural Collection. – Big little books: file of clippings and miscellany. – [Lansing, MI: Michigan State University, 1930-   ] – 1 portfolio. – (Collected at Michigan State University in the Russel B. Nye Popular Culture Collection's Popular Cultural Vertical File, PCVF)

—— —— Popular culture libraries in Florida: University of Florida. – [Lansing, MI: Michigan State University, 1990-   ]. – 1 portfolio (File of correspondence about and drafts of directory entries for this library's collection of comic books and Big Little Books. Listed in RLIF, 1991-   .)

—— —— Popular culture libraries in Illinois: Northwestern University. – [Lansing, MI: Michigan State University, 1982-   ]. – 1 portfolio (File of correspondence about and drafts of directory entries for this library's collection of comic books, Big Little Books, and science fiction. Listed in Anatomy of Wonder (1994-   ), Comics Research Libraries (1988-   ), and RLIF, 1982-   ).

—— —— Popular culture libraries in Minnesota: University of Minnesota. [Lansing, MI: Michigan State University, 1981-   ]. – 1 portfolio (File of correspondence about and drafts of directory entries for this library's collection of Star Trek materials, and science fiction, author manuscripts (Manuscripts Division), and series books, dime novels, comic books and Big Little Books (Children's Literature Research Collections). Listed in Comics Research Libraries (1987-   ), Anatomy of wonder (1987-   ), RLIF, 1982-   ).

Resnick, Michael D. – Official guide to comic books and big little books. [2d ed.] – Florence, AL: House of Collectibles, 1977. – 264 p.

Thomas, James Stuart. – The Big Little Book price guide. – Des Moines, IA: Wallace-Homestead Book Co., c1983. – 160 p.

WEBSITE

www.biglittlebooks.com (The Big Little Book Club)
The Big Little Book Club has been in existence since January of 1982. In that year, six issues of *The Big Little Times,* the club's bi-monthly newsletter, were published by John Stallknecht. All issues from 1983 to the present have been published by Larry Lowery, the current President of the BLB Club and Editor of *The Big Little Times* newsletter.

At the time of this writing, over 1,000 enthusiasts have become members in the club.

The club serves as a conduit of ideas for collectors and dealers. It helps individuals make contacts with other individuals. And it often helps collectors find elusive books at reasonable prices.

Once in a while the club holds a meeting at a toy-and-collectibles show. Meetings in the past have been held in California, Texas, and Maine.

Personal and Corporate Name Index

Fictitious Name Index

Title, Sub-title and Alternate Title Index

Index of Whitman Publishing Company Series Numbers

653.........#15	1102........#70	1144.........#72	1170........#36	1407........#86	1447......#111
W-707 ....#1	1103........#17	*(Second 1100 Series, 1936-1937)*	1171........#38	1409........#96	1448........#89
713.........#24	1107........#37	1146........#34	*(First 1100 Series, 1934-1936)*	1410........#80	1449......#122
715 ....#2	1108........#59	1147........#61	1171........#83	1411........#94	1450......#100
716 ....#6	1112........#57	1148........#90	*(Second 1110 Series, 1936-1937)*	1412......#132	1452......#136
718 ....#9	1114........#78	1149........#52	1172........#48	1413........#117	1453......#113
720.........#11	1116........#14	1150........#21	1173......#101	1420........#85	1455......#134
723.........#27	1117........#65	1151........#35	1175........#39	1421......#127	1456......#128
724..........#4	1118........#60	1152........#49	1177........#29	1422......#119	1457......#115
726.........#20	1120........#66	1153........#44	1178........#33	1424......#102	1458......#135
731 ....#8	1123........#68	1157........#46	1179........#51	1425......#103	1459......#110
742 ....#3	1124........#26	1159........#62	1181........#41	1427........#99	1460......#129
745.........#10	1128........#67	1160........#43	1182........#75	1429......#106	1462......#107
746..........#5	1130........#53	1161........#47	1189........#79	1430......#120	1465......#123
750 ....#7	1133........#55	1162........#40	1190........#58	1432........#81	1466......#118
753.........#18	1135........#76	1163........#69	1191........#71	1433......#116	1467......#133
755.........#19	1136........#73	1164........#87	1192........#54	1434........#88	1471......#124
758.........#22	1140........#16	1166......#108	1193........#77	1435........#91	1477......#126
761.........#25	1141........#23	1167........#42	1194........#56	1438........#95	1480......#114
765.........#12	1142........#45	1169........#32	1198........#64	1440......#109	1488......#131
767.........#30	1143........#63	*(First 1100 Series, 1934-1936)*	1401........#93	1441......#105	1494......#130
768.........#74	1144........#50	1169 ......#104	1403........#97	1442........#92	Buddy Book, 2 ....#125
773.........#31	*(First 1100 Series, 1934-1936)*	*(Second 1100 Series, 1936-1937)*	1404........#82	1444......#112	Cocomalt Edition ..#8.5
776.........#13			1406 ......#121	1445........#98	
779.........#28				1446........#84	

Index of 1981 Lowery Numbers

GW1.........#15	GW52a......#13	GW107......#36	GW153......#68	GW194......#94	GW226......#89
GW2..........#1	GW54 ....#28	GW108......#38	GW157......#67	GW195....#132	GW227....#122
GW6 ....#24	GW57 ....#17	GW109......#48	GW159......#53	GW196....#117	GW228....#100
GW8..........#2	GW61a......#37	GW112......#39	GW160......#76	GW201......#85	GW230....#136
GW9..........#6	GW66 ....#14	GW114......#29	GW161......#73	GW202....#127	GW231....#113
GW11.........#9	GW71a......#26	GW115......#33	GW165......#63	GW203b..#119	GW233....#134
GW13 ....#11	GW76 ....#55	GW116......#51	GW166......#72	GW205....#102	GW234....#128
GW17a.....#27	GW80a......#16	GW118......#41	GW167......#61	GW206....#103	GW235....#115
GW18 ....#4	GW81 ....#23	GW119......#75	GW168......#90	GW208......#99	GW236....#135
GW20 ......#20	GW82 ....#45	GW126......#79	GW171......#62	GW210....#106	GW237....#110
GW21c........#8	GW84a......#50	GW127......#58	GW172......#69	GW211....#120	GW238....#129
GW23 ....#3	GW86a......#34	GW128......#71	GW173......#87	GW213......#81	GW240....#107
GW25 ....#10	GW88 ....#52	GW129......#54	GW175...#108	GW214....#116	GW241....#123
GW26 ....#5	GW89 ....#21	GW130......#77	GW176...#104	GW215......#88	Gw242 ....#118
GW30 ....#7	GW90 ......#35	GW131......#56	GW177......#83	GW216......#91	GW243....#122
GW32 ....#18	GW91 ......#49	GW135......#64	GW179....#101	GW218......#95	GW246....#124
GW34 ....#19	GW92a......#44	GW137......#70	GW184......#93	GW219....#109	GW249b..#126
GW37a.....#22	GW96 ....#46	GW142......#59	GW186......#97	GW220....#105	GW251b..#114
GW40 ....#25	GW98 ....#43	GW145......#57	GW187......#82	GW221......#92	GW254a..#130
GW43 ....#12	GW99 ......#47	GW147......#78	GW189....#121	GW222....#112	GW254b..#131
GW45 ....#30	GW100......#40	GW150......#65	GW190......#86	GW223......#98	GWp13 ....#8.5
GW46 ....#74	GW104......#42	GW151......#60	GW192......#96	GW224......#84	Gwp63 ....#125
GW50 ....#31	GW106......#32	GW152......#66	GW193......#80	GW225....#111	